Choices

A Relapse Prevention Workbook for Female Offenders

by Charlene Steen, Ph.D.

The SaferSociety
PRESS

A program of The Safer Society Foundation, Inc.

ISBN-13: 978-1-884444-75-3
ISBN-10: 1-884444-75-X

Additional copies available from:

A program of the Safer Society Foundation, Inc.
PO Box 340
Brandon, Vermont 05733 USA

(802) 247-3132
www.safersociety.org

Order #WP117 $24.00

10 09 08 07   9 8 7 6 5 4 3 2

Contents

Exercises

Information for Treatment Providers

Research on female offenders, while limited by the much smaller numbers who come to the attention of the criminal justice system, has found a number of notable differences between women and men who commit sexual offenses. Significant among these differences is the fact that a large percentage of females commit their offenses in concert with a male offender (acting in either an active or passive role). These female offenders are usually either coerced or accompanied by a male or may be a compliant observer. They tend to be dependent and nonassertive. Many have been sexual abuse victims themselves (as well as victims of other types of abuse). Either their own children and/or outside children are usually their victims.

Solo female offenders often try to experience intimacy with their own children through sexuality, or they may see themselves as peers of their victims—often teaching adolescent males about sexuality for self-gratification and convincing themselves that they are having a true romantic relationship with their victims.

Females are less likely to commit violent sexual offenses. As opposed to the power/authority issues of male offenders, the bases of female offending often revolve around a lack of satisfying emotional outlets and relationships, a lack of autonomy, loneliness (social alienation, isolation, and inadequate social skills), and low self-esteem. Coercion, misguided expressions of love, and game playing are frequently used to gain victim compliance.

Choices is appropriate for female sex offenders in a variety of settings: outpatient, inpatient, or custodial. Clients who have difficulty writing can complete most of the exercises by responding into a tape recorder or working in tandem with another participant in the program.

This book is designed as an adjunct to group and/or individual therapy with female offenders, not as an end in itself. The concepts and exercises are meant to be processed in the therapeutic setting; thus each chapter and topic should take a number of weeks to cover adequately.

The exercises are designed to reinforce the concepts. They can be discussed and used as a jumping-off point for further discussion about the issues, but practice both in the therapy setting and in the daily living of the client are necessary for adequate assimilation. The summaries at the end of each chapter and the Final Quiz also reinforce the material offered.

The treatment themes are accompanied by specific subtopics as well as the exercises to help the female offender understand, assimilate, and utilize the information being presented.

The contents provide a cognitive-behavioral treatment approach geared to meet female offenders' varied but common needs. Foci are particularly on individuation and the ability to make independent choices and the development of a healthy life style. The sequelae of the offenders' own victimization, how it has affected their lives, and how they can move out of that negative niche are important components. In addition, relapse-prevention and offense-cycle strategies are included as safeguards to prevent recidivism. The themes can also be modified to fit the particular needs of your client.

The purposes of this workbook are to educate female offenders about sexual offending, to help them gain an understanding of their own emotional and psychological processes that led to the abusive behavior, to give them the ability to positively control their own thoughts, feelings, and behaviors by learning to make healthy, informed choices throughout every aspect of their lives, and to increase adequate coping responses. The underlying message is that female offenders have the power to make healthy choices and desist from offending.

There are additional treatment concerns not covered in this book that may be an important part in a specific female sex offender's treatment program. They may include sexual physiology, substance abuse, behavioral reconditioning, and family issues. For some clients, dual or multiple diagnosis work is recommended.

Information for Female Offenders

This workbook, *Choices*, is designed for you to use during and within your sex-offender-specific therapy. You will need some input from your therapist or counselor and from other therapy group members on the topics. It is not a substitute for treatment and should not be used instead of therapy.

There may be other issues you will need to address in treatment so that you can change the negative choices you made to more positive choices for a better life. Substance abuse and its effects, general sexuality information, family issues, and any mental disorders that may affect your behavior are not included in *Choices*. You might be facing other challenges that could respond to outside help.

If you have difficulty reading and understanding what you read, you will need to let your therapist or counselor know, so he or she can arrange for you to complete the book with a tape recorder or assign a helper to you.

There may be some ideas that are difficult to understand as well as some questions or problem-solving exercises that have no clear answers. Your therapist can help you with them.

The most important ideas you will gain from this workbook are:

1) You have the power to choose your lifestyle, your partners, your responses to stress, your thoughts, feelings, and behaviors, and whether to offend or not.

2) There are methods you can use to help you make the right choices.

3) This is a lifetime system you can learn and put into practice for living a healthy, fulfilling life, and preventing yourself from reoffending.

You might find yourself struggling with some of the homework assignments. They're supposed to be hard, so you'll have to really think about how you got to the point of sexually offending or participating in a sexual offense against another person, about why and how your lifestyle was not functioning satisfactorily, and what you can change to keep yourself from getting into similar situations in the future and possibly reoffending.

You may need to do some homework assignments more than once, until your therapist and your treatment group know you've really gotten them. It might help if you either write in pencil so you can change things or write out your first and second tries in a separate notebook that you keep with this book.

By getting treatment and completing this workbook, you've taken a big step in gaining control over your life. With every new choice you make, you'll be on your way toward a more productive, offense-free future and a positive, rewarding life.

Choices: Part I

Understanding My Offenses

Chapter 1

Introduction to a Choice-Based Treatment Program

You are in treatment due to some type of inappropriate or harmful sexual activity. You probably would rather be somewhere else, but a judge made it part of your sentence to be in sex offender treatment during your probation or parole and/or before you can visit with your children or re-unite with them. You must be wondering why you have to be here and what this treatment is all about.

"Why do I need treatment? I've learned my lesson. I'll never commit or participate in a sex offense again."

Every therapist has heard statements like this before. Most of the offenders who say it are honestly sincere and believe what they are saying. But the truth is that without some major change in their lives, many sex offenders do it again, sometimes sooner, sometimes later. Without sex offender treatment, they commit or participate in more violent or more intrusive offenses, or they do it more often to get the same release.

Think of your treatment program and *Choices* as a lifeline, something to hang onto that will guide you to safety when you are headed for trouble. You want to be as sure as you can that you will never participate or be implicated in a sex offense again. Your job now is to learn how to make new, better choices so you can keep your life free from any future sex offenses.

Even if you feel you would never reoffend, you probably have some issues—unhealthy feelings, poor coping strategies, destructive behaviors toward yourself or others, and/or ways of behaving—that you can change, if you want to lead a satisfying and productive life. Your therapy and this workbook are designed to help you look at your life, your thoughts, your feelings, and your choices so you can live in a healthier way. By completing *Choices*, you will be able to build the life you want with more wholesome and satisfying relationships.

But no one can do this for you. You have to be able to and decide to make good choices that will lead to the most positive results possible. That's what this book is about. It was designed to help you help yourself.

We start this book with learning about choices and consequences because healthy, well-thought-out choices are the stepping stones to a healthy, lawful, and fulfilling life. On the other hand, your offending behavior occurred because you made some unhealthy, poorly thought-out choices: who you partnered with and whether to submit to that person's demands, how you met your sexual desires or urges or got your emotional needs met, or failing to stop a partner from hurting your child for whatever reason. Or maybe it was something less direct like choosing to use drugs, which meant you were unable to protect your child. Does one of these situations fit you? If not, take a look at one of the choices you made and why you made it. Talk it over with your therapist and/or group.

Allowing something to happen without saying either yes or no is also making a choice. Letting your faucet drip or your toilet run without turning the tap off or jiggling the handle because you can't decide what to do (Call the landlord? Fix it yourself? Ask a neighbor for help?) is choosing to accept that your water bill will be higher than usual. More active choices also have consequences or results.

You can make choices about almost everything that is ahead of you in life—how you think about things, how you feel, and what you do with those thoughts and feelings. You even have the choice of whether or not to come to therapy.

What comes after choice is another c-word: consequences. Consequences are what happen because of what you did or didn't do. Consequences are the results of a decision, even when that decision is "I can't decide." You might not like the consequences of not coming to therapy because your probation or parole officer might report that you have violated your release conditions and lock you up. Or children's protective services may not let you have your children back. But you have that choice. It's not likely that anyone is going to actually drag you to therapy.

You don't usually get to choose the consequences of what you do. However, the results of many choices are usually predictable. By looking at the situations carefully, you can figure out what the likely consequences of your actions will be and decide if they're what you want. You—and all the rest of us—do this all the time without realizing it. Okay, how many times have you crossed the street when the "Walk" sign wasn't lit? Let's slow down that decision to see how you chose to go ahead.

Before you cross the street, you look left, and then right, and then maybe left again to check for traffic. You figure out how safe it will be to cross over without the light—that is, you look at the likely consequence of your decision to cross—whether the road is clear of traffic and you'll most likely make it safely across, or there's a car coming and you might be hit.

Exercise 1. Choices & Consequences

Think of five choices you made this morning between waking up and eating breakfast. List them below.

1. _____
2. _____
3. _____
4. _____
5. _____

Now think of two consequences or results of each choice and list them below.

1a. _____
1b. _____
2a. _____
2b. _____
3a. _____
3b. _____
4a. _____
4b. _____
5a. _____
5b. _____

As you become more aware of the choices you are actually making and their likely consequences, you can make better choices that lead to healthier and safer results.

Although clearly some choices have very drastic negative consequences, most choices are both good and bad, positive and negative. Sometimes choices look all positive for you, but turn out negative for someone else, and sometimes that negative comes back for you later on.

Chances are, you got something positive from a particular choice or you wouldn't have made it. For example, if you decide not to go to work today, the positive consequences are that you will get to stay in bed later, have some fun time with friends, watch your favorite TV shows, not have to work, and be able to do what you want to do. The negative consequences may include giving up a day's pay, losing your job, disappointing your spouse or significant other (boyfriend or girlfriend), and being unable to pay your bills. And you will probably not be the person selected for a raise or promotion.

If you decide to go to work, the positive consequences are that you will keep your job, be considered responsible, earn money to pay your bills, and maybe even move up in the company. The negative consequences are that you won't be able to sleep late, goof off with friends, or watch television, and you will have to work all day.

There are results that happen right away or very soon after a decision, the "short-term consequences." You decide you want something to eat (decision), you get a box of crackers and a jar of peanut butter (action), you eat some (action), and you feel full (consequence).

There are also results that happen a long time later after you keep making those decisions, the "long-term consequences." you eat a lot of peanut butter and crackers and no vegetables (decision and action), you gain weight (long-term consequence), or your face breaks out because of the oil (long-term consequence), or you get sick because you're not getting enough vitamins in your food (long-term consequence). It can be hard to think way ahead of decisions and actions that look like they will feel good today, but you can learn to think ahead.

There are short-term and long-term consequences to every decision you make. For example, in the work situation, not going to work may give you immediate sleep and pleasure, but mess up your budget and career later.

Exercise 2. Now and Later: Short-term and Long-term Consequences

Think of two choices you've made in the last month. List them or describe the situations below. (Example: I decided to get my hair cut at the "New You" Salon because my neighbor got her hair cut there and it looked really good.)

1. _____

2. _____

List two short-term consequences of each choice: what were the "right-away" or immediate results? They can be positive or negative or one of each. (Example: a. I got rid of my split ends; b. I spent $30 of my grocery money.)

1a. _____

1b. _____

2a. _____

2b. _____

Now think of two things that happened later on as a result of each of your two choices and list them below. (Example: *a.* I felt better about myself and dressed up for my job interview; *b.* I had to go to the food shelf for five meals that month.)

1a. _____

1b. _____

2a. _____

2b. _____

Exercise 3. From Here to There

Can you see how you got from the choice you made to the long-term consequences? See if you can list the steps from your choice to your long-term consequences.

_____

_____

_____

_____

_____

Summary

You can now:

1) Identify choices you make.

2) Recognize some of the short-term and long-term consequences that came from those decisions.

Chapter 2

Self-Understanding

Before you look at the choices you made that led to your offending, it is time to take a more personal look at you—who you are, what you have experienced, thought, and felt, what roles you have played in life, and how you may have broken some of the boundaries of those roles. This chapter will help you understand your actions and sort out what works well for you and what causes you problems, a time to get to know yourself better.

Why is this important? Because until you come to terms with yourself, fully open up your emotions, look at life patterns that contributed to your offending, and build healthy self-esteem, you are at a higher risk of participating in illegal sexual activities again.

A good starting place is to take an inventory of yourself. The inventory can help you see the many different sides of yourself, both on the outside and inside. What do you look like? How do you think? What do you feel about yourself and the world? Where do family and friends fit in? What are your goals, desires, and needs?

The exercise below gives you a format for a self-inventory, starting from the outside in. It is in no way complete, but you may begin to see yourself more clearly after you have described yourself in detail.

Exercise 4. Self-Inventory

1) **General Information:**

   Name: _____

   Age: _____

2) **Physical Characteristics**

   Weight: _____   Height: _____

   Eye color: _____   Hair Color:_____

Is it (Circle answer): Natural/Dyed? Short/Long? Curly/Straight?

Appearance: How would you describe yourself? Look in the mirror if necessary and select and write your answer from the following words: "very," "quite," "somewhat," or "not."

_____ Attractive		_____ Weird	
_____ Ugly		_____ Slender	
_____ Physically fit		_____ Skinny	
_____ Large		_____ Curvy	
_____ Petite		_____ Substantial	
_____ Just right		_____ Heavy	
_____ Well-coordinated		_____ Muscular	
_____ Clumsy		_____ Overweight	
_____ Ordinary		_____ Feminine	
_____ Unusual		_____ Graceful	
_____ Sloppy		_____ Showy	
_____ Well-groomed		_____ Unadorned	
_____ Sporty		_____ Goth	
_____ Glamorous		_____ Leggy	
_____ Sexy		_____ Lumpy	
_____ Sophisticated		_____ Well-proportioned	
_____ Unsophisticated			

How else would you describe your body?

_____

_____

How do you usually dress (conservatively, tough, wild, sexy, all covered up, etc.)?

_____

What is your favorite feature (eyes, hair, nose, ears, breasts, etc.)?

_____

Do others appreciate your appearance? _____ Who?

_____

_____

3) **Mind**: Which words or phrases describe your mental processes? Select and write your answer from the following words: "very," "generally," "sometimes," or "not."

_____ Intelligent   _____ Childish

_____ Street smart   _____ Bored

_____ Sharp (quick)   _____ Scattered

_____ Slow   _____ Focused

_____ Stupid   _____ Ditsy

_____ Talented   _____ Naive (trusting, believing, unworldly)

_____ Clever

_____ Thoughtful   _____ Good sense of humor

_____ Capable   _____ Creative (at what?)

_____ Funny   _____

_____ Sophisticated   _____ Other

_____ Imaginative   _____

_____ Mature

What do you like most about your mind?

_____

Do others appreciate your mind? _____ Who?

_____

4) **Feelings**: Describe your feelings by writing in one of the following words: "very," "generally," "somewhat," or "not."

_____	Happy	_____	Self-centered
_____	Sad/Depressed	_____	Caring of others
_____	Angry	_____	Unfeeling
_____	Frustrated	_____	Explosive
_____	Strong	_____	Calm
_____	Weak	_____	Passive
_____	Emotional	_____	Tired
_____	Nervous/Anxious	_____	Energetic
_____	Lonely	_____	Bitter
_____	Loved	_____	Serious
_____	Well-liked	_____	Lighthearted
_____	Independent	_____	Fearless
_____	Needy	_____	Scared
_____	Bored	_____	Self-confident
_____	Lively	_____	Insecure

Are there any other feeling words that would describe you?

_____

_____

What do you like most about the way you feel?

_____

_____

Are there ways you would rather feel? _____ What are they?

_____

_____

Do others appreciate the good ways you feel? _____ Who?

_____

_____

What do they appreciate?

_____

_____

Describe some times when you felt really good.

_____

_____

_____

5) **Behavior**: How would you describe your general behavior? Select and write your answer from the following words: "usually," "often," "sometimes," or "not."

What other words or phrases describe your behavior?

_____

_____

_____ Obedient		_____ Daring
_____ Respectful		_____ Honest
_____ Conservative		_____ Trustworthy
_____ Wild		_____ Loner
_____ Irresponsible		_____ Self-sufficient
_____ "Cool"		_____ Meek
_____ Sexy		_____ Cheap
_____ Ready to fight		_____ Classy
_____ Friendly		_____ Defiant
_____ Aggressive		_____ Leader
_____ Stand up for self		_____ Do what others want
_____ Stand up for others		_____ Overly responsible

_____ Cruel

_____ Kind

_____ User

_____ Impulsive

_____ Compulsive

_____ Impatient

_____ Patient

_____ Loser

_____ Winner

_____ Good at sports

_____ Quick learner

_____ Good lover

_____ Good friend

_____ Good worker

_____ Enjoy playing around

_____ Tease

_____ Gossip

_____ Can keep secrets

_____ Blow up often

_____ Fight a lot

_____ Steal

_____ Cheat

_____ Sleep around

_____ Prostitute

_____ Sex addict

_____ Controlling

_____ Alcoholic

_____ Drug addict

_____ Celebrity

_____ Follower

_____ Take or do what I want no matter how it affects others

6) **Family**: Describe the family you grew up in by writing in one of the following: "mostly," "somewhat," "a little," or "not." (Include natural, adoptive, and stepparents, natural and stepbrothers and sisters, grandparents or other relatives with whom you lived as you were growing up. Do not include foster family members.)

_____ Close

_____ Distant

_____ Important to me

_____ Trustworthy

_____ Well-adjusted

_____ Dysfunctional

_____ There for me

_____ Not available

_____ Good listeners

_____ Rigid

_____ Flexible

_____ Smothering

_____ Shaming

_____ Hurtful

_____ Mean

_____ Abusive

_____ Fair

_____ Respectful

_____ Embarrassing

_____ Fun to be with

_____ Boring

_____ Caring

_____ Smart

_____ Stupid

_____ Cruel

_____ Insensitive

_____ Loyal

_____ Chaotic

_____ Calm

_____ Fun

_____ Intellectual

_____ Good at sports

_____ Mechanical

_____ Artistic

_____ Clever

_____ Angry

_____ Strict

_____ Demanding

_____ Religious

_____ Law abiding

_____ Lawbreakers (who?)

_____

_____ Clean and sober

_____ Alcoholics (who?)

_____

_____ Successful

_____ Drug users (who?)

_____

_____ TV couch potatoes (who?)

_____

_____ Workaholics (who?)

_____

_____ Sex Addicts (who?)

_____

Do any of your family members come to you for help or a listening ear? Who?

_____

Are you a lot like any of your family members? If yes, who?

_____

Are you very different from most of the others? How?

_____

How would you have changed your family if you could?

_____

_____

_____

7) **Spouse or Significant Other:** If you are or were married or in a significant relationship with someone, answer the same questions about your current or past spouse or significant other, writing in one of the following words: "mostly," "somewhat," "a little," or "not."

_____ Close		_____ Abusive	
_____ Distant		_____ Fair	
_____ Important to me		_____ Respectful	
_____ Trustworthy		_____ Embarrassing	
_____ Well-adjusted		_____ Fun to be with	
_____ Dysfunctional		_____ Boring	
_____ There for me		_____ Caring	
_____ Unavailable		_____ Smart	
_____ Good listener		_____ Stupid	
_____ Rigid		_____ Cruel	
_____ Flexible		_____ Insensitive	
_____ Smothering		_____ Loyal	
_____ Shaming		_____ Chaotic	
_____ Hurtful		_____ Calm	
_____ Mean		_____ Fun	

_____ Intellectual   _____ Selfish

_____ Good at sports   _____ Demanding

_____ Mechanical   _____ Supportive

_____ Artistic   _____ Impotent

_____ Clever   _____ Sexy

_____ Angry   _____ Alcoholic?

_____ Law abiding   In recovery? _____

_____ Lawbreaker (now or previously?) _____ Drug user? What type of drugs?

_____   _____

_____ Religious   In recovery? _____

_____ Successful

Anything else that describes that person?

_____

_____

How would you change your spouse or significant other if you could?

_____

_____

_____

_____

8) **Your Life**: What is important to you? Select and write your answer from the following words: "very," "quite," "somewhat," or "not."

_____ Friends

_____ Being well-known

_____ Being invisible

_____ Being part of a group

_____ Being independent/
self-sufficient

_____ Being liked

_____ Keeping in shape

_____ Looking beautiful

_____ Affection

_____ Love

_____ Sex

_____ Sports

_____ Music

_____ Other arts

_____ Creativity

_____ Making things (What?)

_____

_____ Knowing a lot

_____ Money

_____ Possessions

_____ Travel

_____ Being a mom

_____ Relationship(s)

_____ Career

_____ Freedom

_____ Rules

_____ Being unique

_____ Fitting in

_____ Partying

_____ Personal growth

_____ Politics

_____ Security

_____ Excitement

_____ Variety

_____ Consistency

_____ Other things

_____

What are you currently doing to get most of the things above that are important to you?

_____

_____

Are there things you could do to get the important things but aren't doing? What?

_____

_____

_____

What seems to get in the way or stop you?

_____

_____

_____

9) **Analysis**: Carefully read all you have written above. See how it all fits together. You may have a little better picture of yourself—who you are, how you think, feel, and act, what your roots are, and what is important to you in life.

What would you like to change?

_____

_____

_____

What can you do to improve these things? (You may not be able to totally change some, but you can often make improvements, especially in your own thoughts, feelings, and behaviors.)

_____

_____

_____

10) **Goals**: For this last section, imagine your life as you would like it to be ten years from now. Be realistic. Then write your answers to these questions.

Where will you be living?

_____

Who will you be living with?

_____

Will you be married or in a relationship?

_____

Will you have (more) children?

_____

Will you have pets or farm animals?

_____

_____

Will you have any further education? If so, in what subjects?

_____

_____

What will you be doing for work? Or will you be retired?

_____

_____

What will your money situation be?

_____

_____

How will you have fun?

_____

_____

What kind of social life will you have?

_____

_____

What kinds of projects will you be doing or be part of?

_____

_____

What kinds of relationships will you have?

_____

_____

What will you look like?

_____

_____

Where and how will you travel?

_____

_____

What will your spiritual life be like?

_____

_____

How will you be helping others?

_____

_____

What will your most important possessions be?

_____

_____

Other?

_____

_____

Think of these as your goals. Goals are simply what you want your life to be like. You can achieve almost all of them if you work toward the steps to attain them. Write these goals out separately on a piece of paper or card and tack them up somewhere where you will look at them frequently. It is important not to forget about them. You will probably adjust some of them, as your desires change and as time goes on. But always keep them in the back of your mind and think about them as you make choices that will affect your life. By setting realistic goals and making good choices, your life will have some direction, and you will be less likely to hurt others or get into trouble.

Summary

You can now:

1) Better understand who you are—your physical, mental, emotional, behavioral, and family characteristics, your life and what is important to you, what you want to change, and what your goals are.

2) Begin to understand how these characteristics can help you make better choices in the future.

Chapter 3

Victimization

Everyone is a victim in big ways or small ways at some time in their lives. Women who have participated in a sexual offense are much more likely to have been victims of serious abuse—sexual, physical, and/or emotional—than women who have never committed a sex crime and more likely than men who commit sex crimes. Being victimized affects feelings, thoughts, and behaviors. These experiences disturb reality and impair a person's ability to feel, think, and respond appropriately to life's circumstances.

Being victimized is never an excuse or justification for victimizing others. It is important to look at your victimization, however, as a means to help you understand your transition from victim to victimizer, to see the patterns of behavior that led to your offense, so that you don't repeat the patterns and hurt anyone again.

But first let's look at exactly what a victim is and how you know if you have been or are being victimized.

In defining the word "victim," the dictionary includes the following:

1) A person who suffers from a destructive or injurious action

2) A person who is deceived or cheated

As a human being, you have no doubt been victimized in both senses of the word. As a perpetrator or participant in a sex offense, you have victimized others in the same ways. You may feel that you have been cheated somehow by your family, your boss, or "the system," that you are the real injured party in your case. This kind of thinking is "poor me" thinking, or taking a victim stance. This is a thinking error that contributes to your offense cycle. As we talk about your victimization, be careful not to fall into "poor me" thinking errors. When you committed or participated in a sex offense, you caused your victim to suffer from a destructive or injurious action. You might have denied it or rationalized it away at the time, or you still may not quite believe that your victim suffered great harm from what you did or didn't do.

"Abuse" is the destructive or injurious action suffered by victims. It can take the form of sexual abuse, including molestation or rape—even by a partner; physical abuse, which includes beatings, hair pulling, burning, and all kinds of torture; emotional abuse, which includes all types of verbal and/or nonverbal messages that say you are no good, worthless, unloved, etc, and can include neglect, in which your needs for food, clothing, shelter, love, affection, etc. , are withheld by a person responsible for giving them to you.

Knowing that you've been abused and understanding how it affected you can help you understand your offending behavior and help you to not do it again. But it is important to stress again that having been a victim is not an excuse for self-pity or destructive behavior, and it is never an excuse for sexual offending.

Experiences people have usually color their view of the world and the way they function. In addition, they often think that such experiences are normal and usual, experienced by everyone else. Because of this, victims may have shut down painful feelings in order to survive, and they may not be aware of how they are hurting people they victimize. But *why* do women who were abused turn around and sexually abuse or participate in the sexual abuse of someone else? There are a number of explanations. See which one best fits your situation.

Shut-down emotions: You may have needs that you satisfied by sex offending, and you rationalized away the harm you did by saying to yourself, "I experienced that, and it didn't hurt me." When you think that way, you are usually showing that you have shut down your emotions. Because what you felt when you were sexually or physically abused was probably extremely uncomfortable or painful, you stuffed the emotions down so deeply that you no longer feel them. You didn't pay attention to the fact that you would be victimizing someone when you committed your sex offense because you lost touch with how you felt—upset, hurt, or confused—during and/or after you were victimized.

Love and attention: Sometimes you might have felt both good and bad feelings during a sexual molestation. For example, if you didn't get the love and attention you needed when you were a child, you might have felt that the only time you ever got them was when you were molested. Then you rationalized your own molesting behavior as giving love or attention to your victim.

Rage: If you were physically beaten, raped, molested, and/or brutalized in some other way, you might have felt rage from the violence and unfairness perpetrated against you, and you might have needed an outlet for your angry feelings. By acting these emotions out in a sexual way on someone else without considering what your victim could be feeling, you might have satisfied this need to express your rage.

Power: You might have stepped into the shoes of your perpetrator who was all powerful at the time. When you were molested, you might have felt very powerless. And now, when you feel powerless as an adult, you commit an act that you remember made your perpetrator powerful and that gives you the same feelings of power and control.

Intimacy: You might have felt so inadequate and worthless because you were (or are being) put down and verbally abused that you feel no adult could ever be attracted to you. So you put your own needs first, using a child who gives you his or her attention and love to meet your needs for intimacy and sexuality. Your own neediness overrides your awareness that you are victimizing another.

Impaired thinking: You might have used substances (alcohol and drugs) that muddied your thinking and dulled the pain, so that your conscience didn't kick in and stop you from doing what you knew was wrong.

Sexual addiction: Or you might have been sexually molested over and over again at an early age and now feel like you need sexual gratification, like a video-game junkie needs Nintendo, and the only way you can get it is by molesting a child or exposing yourself, or by some other type of sexual offense.

These are just a few of the reasons victims become victimizers. If you were a victim, do any of these fit for you? Which one(s)?

_____

_____

What do you think your victim felt during the abuse you (and others) did to him/her?

_____

_____

What do you think kept you from heeding what your victim was most likely feeling?

_____

_____

No matter which of the scenarios above (or perhaps another not listed here) fit you, unless you truly don't care if you hurt another person, which is very uncommon, your own victimization might have kept you from understanding and connecting with the painful emotions your victim might have felt and the effects he/she might have suffered. Otherwise, you probably wouldn't have sexually offended because you are basically a good person and good people try not to hurt others.

There are some people, however, who are so filled with rage, wanting to get back at people who hurt them, that they deliberately hurt others. They, especially, need to better understand the sources of that rage and healthier ways to express it.

The histories below are true examples of harmful or injurious experiences of some offenders who didn't really understand the pain and problems their own abuse or victimization caused them. The last scenario deals with another way people handle severe abuse called dissociation, or going away in their minds.

Read these six histories carefully. Do any parts of them seem similar to what happened to you or what you did? Even if they do not seem similar, can you see how you lost touch with your feelings about your own abuse? Can you see how your victim might have felt? (You will have an opportunity a little later in this chapter to really analyze your own abuse.)

As you read these stories, remember that not all people who experienced abuse then abuse someone else. Most victims are *not* perpetrators. It is important to keep reminding yourself that abuse is not an excuse for offending against others. Looking at any victimization you might have experienced gives you information about where some of your thoughts and feelings come from. You can then use this information to help understand and change your thoughts, feelings, and behavior and prevent yourself from reoffending.

1) Carolina's parents were unskilled workers who made minimum wage. To support their family, they each held two full-time jobs. By the time they came home from work, they were too tired to do much more than go to bed. Consequently, there was nobody to hold, love, and mother Carolina, who was the youngest of five children and the only girl.

Two of her older brothers began to simulate sexual intercourse by rubbing themselves on top of Carolina when she was about four and they were young teenagers. Gradually, this developed into full sexual intercourse. Carolina didn't like having intercourse with her brothers, but sometimes she would go up to them and rub against them so they would have sex with her because she didn't know any other way to get them to give her the affection she craved.

Carolina married early to get away from home, had a little girl, and then divorced. She was feeling very lonely and unloved, so she began to kiss and touch and digitally penetrate her daughter sexually. She rationalized this as giving her daughter the love and affection the child needed.

2) Angela's father was an alcoholic. When she was growing up, her father would come home drunk and throw things. Often she had to dodge flying lamps, ashtrays, books, and dishes. Once he didn't miss, and Angela was cut by a glass ashtray and had to have stitches. Angela's father usually didn't remember what he had done and always apologized the next day. Angela's mother said her father was a good man but suffered from the disease of alcoholism. Angela didn't think she was abused because several of her friends' fathers did the same thing, and besides, her father didn't know what he was doing. She believed her father loved her. Angela was not sexually abused.

After Angela had a baby, the child's father deserted her. One day, Angela was feeling tired and frustrated and her infant son would not stop crying. So she painfully yanked and twisted his penis and stuck her finger up his anus.

3) Since their father didn't help or come around at all, Victoria's mother had to raise her children alone. She had a hard time making ends meet and would get really frustrated when she felt that the children—especially Victoria—were stirring up trouble or not trying hard enough. Victoria had problems in school because of her learning disorder. She was smart, but couldn't read or write very well. Because school was so hard for her, she often wouldn't try. Her mother got very angry with her when she refused to do her homework and brought home bad reports from school. She yelled at Victoria, "You are stupid! You will never amount to anything! You are just as worthless as your father!" Victoria thought her mother was probably right. She began to hang out with the stoners at school, drinking and using whatever substances she could get her hands on, and she eventually dropped out of school.

When she was sixteen, she met and moved in with John, a considerably older man who took care of her. They enjoyed getting loaded together. One night, John invited the thirteen-year-old neighbor boy into their house, offering him some pot. When the child was pretty well stoned, he told Victoria to have sex with the boy while he (John) masturbated. Victoria didn't want to, but she was afraid John would leave her if she didn't do what he said. This went on several times over the next year or two, until the boy told a friend, who told a teacher, who called the police.

4) Barbie and her mother lived together by themselves. Her mother was a stripper and wasn't around much. When Barbie was a child, she watched her mother do erotic dances in the nude at a club and get all kinds of attention and money. Barbie wanted love and attention too. She became a nude model when she was eighteen and loved her job. She would deliberately leave her clothes off longer than she needed to when her modeling was over, often striking sexual poses to get patrons to notice her. One day she was modeling for the life-drawing class at a college. The students didn't seem to pay much attention to her, so during a break, she decided to stroll down the campus in the nude. She was surprised when she was arrested for indecent exposure since her actions didn't seem at all sexual.

5) Kanesha was sexually and physically abused as a child, and felt she somehow must be so worthless that she deserved it. She hated school because the other kids made fun of her ugly clothes and frizzy hair. She dropped out early and ran around with guys who were also misfits. They were often in and out of jail. She hooked up with a guy named Mickey, who she thought really loved her. But once they started living together, he began to batter her. Since she had nowhere else to go,

she stayed in the relationship. They had two children together. When their oldest daughter was five, Mickey started sexually abusing the child. Kanesha caught him and told him to stop, but he beat Kanesha bloody. Kanesha tried to leave with the kids once, but she was terribly lonely and missed Mickey, so she returned. He started molesting their daughter again. Kanesha didn't think she could live without him, and she was afraid that if she tried to stop him, he would kill her. So she stayed put and did nothing about it.

When their daughter was eight, she told the Child Abuse Prevention teacher what was happening and that her mother knew and was even in the room when it was happening, but didn't protect her. Kanesha and Mickey were both arrested. Mickey went to prison. The charges were dropped against Kanesha, but she was declared an unfit mother and the children were taken away. She was required by Children's Protective Services to complete an outpatient sex-offender treatment program before she could have any contact with her children.

6) Marion's mother and stepfather treated her horrendously. They chained her under the house and when Marion wasn't quick enough to obey, her stepfather bent her over and forcibly had anal sex with her (anal sex, also called "sodomy" or "sodomizing," is when a male puts his penis in a person's bottom, or anus). They beat her bloody with belts and chains, and killed her pet dog in front of her. When Marion was being abused, she would black out, and another part of her would take over, a part that didn't feel anything. Marion's way to survive was by dissociation. That is, she lost herself and her memories. She detached herself from her feelings and even from conscious awareness in order to get through the abuse. She honestly had no memory of being abused, or possibly even abusing. (This is a little different from what happens when people deny their own history of abuse and their abuse of others. People who deny are aware that they were abused and are abusing, but are afraid or ashamed to admit it. A less severe form of dissociation is when people know they were abused, but feel like it wasn't happening to them, like they were floating somewhere above and watching it from a distance.)

Marion was taken away from her home by the state when she was eleven. She had no memory of what had happened to her before she was placed in foster care. Her foster mother said she had severe attention problems and stole things. Marion had no idea how she got the stolen objects. She had no memory of stealing them. She said she "spaced out" and found herself in clothes she didn't remember putting on and in locations she didn't remember traveling to.

Marion was arrested five years later for putting sticks up the anus of a three-year-old child in the foster home. She had no memory of doing anything. After spending several years in California Youth Authority, she was released. She didn't have much treatment because she was labeled a "denier." A year after her release, she pushed a hairbrush and scissors up the anus of a three-year-old child she was babysitting, causing permanent injury. She has no memory of what happened during that crime. She has no feelings about either abusing or being abused. She has no idea what her victims might have felt. She still has no memory at all of her early childhood.

This last example is very extreme, but the facts come from a true case. While many victims report forgetting about being abused for a number of years, it is much less common not to remember abusing others in the present. Most people who claim not to remember abusing others usually know what they did. They deny their offense to protect themselves because of fear, shame, and guilt, or to avoid the consequences of their actions.

To review: All six of these people were abused in some way and abused others. The abuse they suffered caused them emotional or physical pain at the time (even if they closed off the feelings or forgot about the abuse) and was destructive to them. Even though some of them minimized what happened to them (perhaps because they wanted it not to matter, wanted to avoid feeling the pain, or wanted to be tough), the abuse caused problems for them and others later on. The abuse they experienced was one of the contributing factors when they abused others. The abuse left them with feelings of rage, fear, emptiness, and/or powerlessness, and/or it skewed how they got their needs for affection, love, and intimacy met. They acted out their feelings and needs by sexually abusing others. Because they were not aware of how damaging the abuse they had suffered was to them, they didn't understand the hurt they caused their victims.

Let's look at each of these histories a little more closely. In the first case, Carolina had been deprived of normal non-sexual love and affection by her parents and siblings. The only way she could get any closeness was by submitting to sexual abuse. If her brothers had been appropriately loving and affectionate and not sexually abusive, she could have gotten this love and affection in a healthy way. She closed down her painful feelings so much that she did not understand that her victim might feel frightened, sickened, or powerless in the situation. She didn't even realize that her daughter might have agreed to participate because her daughter wanted the same kind of approval and caring from Carolina that Carolina had wanted from her brothers.

In the second history, Angela was probably terrified for her own safety as a young girl and furious at what her father was putting her through. But she could never recognize and express her feelings of powerlessness and anger because her father kept apologizing and her mother kept making excuses for her father's behavior. So these feelings built up, and when Angela became a mother and felt frustrated, angry, and helpless about her situation, she took her feelings out on her child. Because Angela's fear and anger were never acknowledged, she didn't appreciate how terrified and helpless her little boy might feel. She didn't even have any idea why she did it.

In the third history, Victoria was put down again and again because of her mother's frustrations. She hated school because of her learning disorder, and she was angry at her mother and furious with herself. She believed it when her mother told her she was worthless. She felt that nobody could love, understand, or help her. She felt inadequate and unwanted and hung out with people who felt the same way and used substances to dull the pain of rejection. Because an older man wanted her, she became dependent on him to meet her needs. She didn't believe she could make it on her own and was terrified of being abandoned. So she did whatever the man wanted in order to keep him. The substances she used probably dulled her conscience, and she probably told herself that the neighbor boy liked the abuse because he returned to their home.

In the fourth history, Barbie was exposed to erotic nudity at too young an age and in an inappropriate way. Because Barbie was out of touch with her own needs for attention and excitement, she acted out her feelings the same way her mother did. Barbie forgot how uncomfortable she felt watching her mother gyrating sexually in the nude and only thought of the excitement of doing it. She didn't think striking sexual poses and running around nude on the campus would upset anyone.

In the fifth history, Kanesha felt inadequate, bad, and worthless due to her childhood abuse. Like Victoria in the third vignette, she hung around with other misfits who felt the same way. When she met Mickey, he had been loving and caring at first. It wasn't until she was pregnant with their first child that he began to hit her. At first, they would have a loving reconciliation after each abusive incident. Then he gradually began to beat her up more frequently and with greater force. But she was too dependent on him to leave, since she didn't think she deserved better and didn't think she could make it on her own. In addition, she was terrified of what he might do if he found her after she left. She felt helpless to stop him from molesting their daughter, but she didn't think she was doing anything wrong, since she was not the one doing the molesting.

In the final history, Marion was the subject of such severe abuse that she literally shut down her emotions and her consciousness in order to survive. At times later on, when she was in a safer situation, her rage at what happened to her would take over. She wasn't even aware of what she was feeling. Sometimes she wasn't even aware of what she was doing. She had a dissociative disorder that fragmented her personality, so she felt like she was two different people. Her separation from her own feelings when she was abused prevented her from recognizing or caring about what her victim might feel. Because she was the most out of touch with what happened to her and what she did, she was at the highest risk of repeating her sexually offending behavior and of its escalating into even more serious behavior—possibly even murder.

Do you think you were abused when you were a child? What happened? Who did it? Was there some reason given for why you were being abused? How did you feel? Write about some of your childhood experiences. Telling the story can help you begin to connect feelings and thoughts to how you choose to act.

_____

_____

_____

_____

_____

_____

_____

_____

_____

_____

_____

_____

_____

_____

_____

Exercise 6, on the following page, gives you the opportunity to examine whether your own childhood experiences were abusive.

Write "yes" on the blank line next to the items that apply to you. Think about how often they happened. Were they everyday or rare occurrences? Write "no" next to anything listed that did not happen to you.

1) **Physical Abuse**

   a) How were you punished or treated when you were a child? Were you or have you ever been…?

   _____ Hit with a belt

   _____ Hit with kitchen utensils

   _____ Hit with a stick

   _____ Hit with a coat hanger

   _____ Struck with closed fists

   _____ Hit by thrown objects

   _____ Kicked

   _____ Painfully pinched

   _____ Painfully tickled

   _____ Burned

   _____ Cut

   _____ Drugged

   _____ Thrown across the room or against a wall

   _____ Choked

   _____ Held with your head under water (sink, toilet, pool, stream)

   _____ Tied or chained up

   _____ Forced to stay out in the cold

   _____ Beaten with cords or whips

   _____ Starved (not just missed a meal)

   _____ Made to eat out of the dog or cat's dish or off the floor

   _____ Made to stand or kneel in a painful or uncomfortable position for a long period of time

   Have you ever…?

   _____ Had your hair pulled out

   _____ Had your head hit against the wall or floor

   _____ Had food forcibly stuffed down your throat

   _____ Other:

   _____

   _____

All of these types of punishment are abusive. If they, or any similar abusive physical acts were perpetrated against you, you are a victim of physical abuse. This is also true if you were an adult at the time of the abuse.

b) Who did this to you?

_____

c) If you were a victim of physical abuse, how did you feel during the time you were being abused?

_____ Angry	_____ Unwanted
_____ Afraid	_____ Powerless
_____ Sad	_____ Strong enough to take it
_____ Bad	_____ Humiliated
_____ I deserved it	_____ No feelings at all
_____ Picked on	_____ Other:
_____ Worthless	_____
_____ Unloved	_____

d) How did you feel right after the abuse?

_____ Angry	_____ Like getting even
_____ Afraid	_____ Like "you can't get to me"
_____ Sad	_____ Frustrated
_____ Bad	_____ Wanting to run away
_____ Picked on	_____ Obedient
_____ Worthless	_____ More disobedient
_____ Unloved	_____ Other:
_____ Unwanted	_____
_____ Nervous	_____

e) Did you or do you...?

_____ Fight a lot

_____ Have a quick, hot temper

_____ Often hit your brothers or sisters

_____ Punch walls

_____ Hit your spouse or significant other

_____ Throw objects

_____ Take it out on your children or animals

_____ Kick things

_____ Get even with people who cross you

_____ Not get close to anyone

_____ Think most people are out to get you

_____ Hate most people

_____ Feel like you deserved the abuse

_____ Not care

_____ Want to beat up your perpetrator

_____ Act bad

_____ Have other negative behaviors:

_____

_____

2) Sexual Abuse

a) Violent sex: Did anyone ever use force or threats to...?

_____ Rape you (intercourse)

_____ Sodomize you (anal sex)

_____ Feel you up (fondling)

_____ Make you perform oral sex

_____ Perform oral sex on you

_____ Masturbate you

_____ Make you look at his/her sexual parts

_____ Make you masturbate him/her

_____ Grab any of your sexual parts

_____ Insert objects inside you

_____ Take sexual photographs of you

_____ Make you watch sexual acts

_____ Make you participate in pornographic films

_____ Make you have sex with others for money or gifts (prostitution)

_____ Make you have sex with animals

_____ Make you perform group sex acts

_____ Make you do anything sexual with yourself.

_____ Other

_____

_____

What?

_____

Who did this to you?

_____

What force or threat of force did they use?

_____

_____

Were you sexually aroused? (This is a normal reaction.) _____

Do you feel sexual feelings now when you think about being sexually abused?

_____

_____

b) Coercive sex: Did anyone with more power or status convince, bribe, or trick you to do or submit to any of the following acts?

_____ Sexual intercourse

_____ Rub up against you

_____ Anal sex (sodomy)

_____ Prostitute yourself

_____ Masturbate him/her

_____ Perform group sex acts

_____ Masturbate him/herself in front of you

_____ Perform sex for others

_____ Feel you up (fondling)

_____ Tickle your sexual areas

_____ Let him/her masturbate you

_____ Teach you about sex by showing you how to do it

_____ Put his penis between your legs

_____ Take sexual photos of you

_____ Put his/her mouth on your sexual parts

_____ Show you pornographic books or movies

_____ Make you have oral sex with him/her

_____ Have sex with animals

_____ Pretend to touch your sexual parts for a medical reason

_____ Put any objects into your anus or vagina

_____ Make you undress and spank you

_____ Make you undress and   _____ Other:
          humiliate you

_____

_____

Who did this to you?

_____

How did that person get you to go along?

_____

_____

_____

_____

Did you feel sexually aroused by the acts? (This is a normal reaction.)

_____

_____

Did you feel close or loved?

_____

Did you miss the sexuality when it stopped? (This is also a normal reaction.) _____

Do you feel sexual feelings now when you think about when you were sexually coerced?

_____

_____

    c) *Attempted* sexual acts: Did anyone ever *try* to do any of the above to you or with you? (This is sexual abuse, too.) _____

       If so, which acts?

_____

_____

_____

    d) Did you ever go along with being sexual with someone when you really wanted to say no or stop? _____

When? _____

With whom? _____

Why? _____

e) How did you feel when the sexual abuse activity you listed was happening? (You may have many or mixed feelings, good and bad.)

_____	Afraid	_____	Special
_____	Uncomfortable	_____	Chosen
_____	Embarrassed	_____	Sexy
_____	In shock	_____	Aroused
_____	Not there (dissociated)	_____	Attractive
_____	Special	_____	Furious
_____	Confused	_____	Guilty
_____	Angry	_____	Guilty but aroused
_____	Powerless	_____	Ashamed
_____	Weird	_____	Important
_____	Helpless	_____	Different from others
_____	Terrified	_____	Mature
_____	No good	_____	Powerful
_____	Deserving of it	_____	Loved
_____	Picked on	_____	Hated
_____	Scarred for life	_____	Other:
_____	Dirty	_____	
_____	Unloved		

f) How do you feel about it now?

_____ Angry

_____ Still afraid

_____ Sad

_____ Bad

_____ Used

_____ Worthless

_____ Scarred

_____ Like it was no big deal

_____ Guilty

_____ Humiliated

_____ Embarrassed

_____ Unloved

_____ Special

_____ Lonely

_____ Powerless

_____ Mature

_____ Different from others

_____ Smarter than others

_____ Disgusted

_____ Sexier

_____ Cheap

_____ Stupid

_____ Often depressed

_____ Deserving of it

_____ Confused

_____ Ripped off of some of my childhood

_____ Other:

_____

_____ Nothing

g) How might the sexual abuse have affected you? Do you…?

_____ Stay alone a lot	_____ Miss work a lot
_____ Need to be with people	_____ Have to be perfect
_____ Drink a lot	_____ Mistrust others
_____ Use drugs	_____ Get sick a lot
_____ Have a hot temper	_____ Use food to avoid feelings
_____ Fight a lot	_____ Get even
_____ Run away from home	_____ Act tough
_____ Have trouble concentrating	_____ Break rules
_____ Daydream a lot	_____ Break the law
_____ Hold feelings in	_____ Hurt others
_____ Go along with anything (not say no)	_____ Not care about the future
	_____ Think about suicide
_____ Avoid sex	_____ Attempt suicide
_____ Think about sex all the time	_____ Destroy things (yours or somone else's?)
_____ Have sex more often than others	
_____ Have less sex than others	_____ Have difficulty making close relationships
_____ Use sex to get things	_____ Other:
_____ Constantly masturbate	_____
_____ Use pornography	_____ No effect
_____ Put yourself down	

3) **Emotional Abuse:** Write down names you were called and things that were said or done to you that have made you see yourself in a negative light. While everyone has been put down in some way, if these things happened on a regular basis, they can be considered emotional abuse. You will have the opportunity to decide afterward if they reached the level of emotional abuse.

Names Called	Things Said	Nonverbal Messages
(like "stupid," "slut," racial slurs, or social put-downs)	(like "you'll never amount to anything")	(like always doing things for your sibling[s] but never for you)

By Father:

_____ _____ _____

_____ _____ _____

_____ _____ _____

_____ _____

By Mother:

_____ _____ _____

_____ _____ _____

_____ _____ _____

_____ _____

By a Stepparent:

_____ _____ _____

_____ _____ _____

_____ _____ _____

_____ _____ _____

By Other Family Members:

_____ _____ _____

_____ _____ _____

_____ _____ _____

_____ _____ _____

By a Teacher:

_____ _____ _____

_____ _____ _____

_____ _____ _____

_____ _____ _____

By Classmates:

_____   _____   _____

_____   _____   _____

_____   _____   _____

_____   _____   _____

By Others:

_____   _____   _____

_____   _____   _____

_____   _____   _____

_____   _____   _____

1) How often were you given these negative messages? Talk about this with your friends and group members. Then think about it carefully. Do you think that you were called names, put down, or given negative non-verbal or subtle messages a lot of the time? Then decide—have you been emotionally abused…?

_____ Constantly?

_____ Often?

_____ Some of the time?

2) How do you think the put-downs you have experienced have affected your life (even if they didn't reach the level of emotional abuse)? Do you think you may:

_____ Have lower self-esteem

_____ Have fewer goals

_____ Have less friends

_____ Be more depressed

_____ Feel more frustrated

_____ Not try

_____ Use alcohol more

_____ Use other drugs more

_____ Feel angrier

_____ Feel stupid

_____ Feel helpless

_____ Feel resentful

_____ Try harder

_____ Feel like a loser

_____ Rebel more

_____ Care less about what happens to you

_____ Care less about others

_____ Care less about everything

_____ Get along worse with family

_____ Want to put one over on everyone

_____ Commit criminal acts

_____ Other

_____

_____

Read this exercise over once a week or once a month. It is good to put the past behind you, but you need to process (or work through) the thoughts and feelings you felt during and after the abuse you experienced. This means you need to identify the feelings and thoughts relative to your abuse and express them to your therapist, group, and anyone else your therapist recommends. You can express them by talking about them, writing, drawing, or painting them, and/or acting them out. When you have really identified these thoughts and feelings and expressed them thoroughly, gaining control over your past experiences, they are less likely to influence what you think, feel, and do, particularly about sexual offending. If you were victimized (abused), you may be blaming yourself instead of the perpetrator, thinking yourself stupid to have let it go on. Or you may be acting out some of the rage you feel instead of working through it in a healthy way.

If you have been abused physically, sexually, or emotionally and you have no feelings about it or feel it was no big deal, you are probably out of touch with your feelings and need more work to zero in on them. You are much more likely to commit another sex offense or another hurtful act if you are unaware of your anger, frustration, lack of self-esteem, or other feelings left over from the abuse you received. If you don't understand your feelings, you will not see the signs leading to reoffense. Unless you notice them, you cannot change your thoughts, feelings, and behaviors to avoid or escape risky situations.

You might not have been sexually, physically, or emotionally abused as a child, or any abuse you experienced might have been minimal or a minor, isolated experience. Not everyone who sexually abuses others experienced abuse as a child. As you talk to other friends, you will find that some experienced terrible abuse but never acted out in a hurtful way, and they seem to get along pretty well. On the other hand, many people who were *not* seriously abused committed sex offenses or other criminal acts. Everyone reacts differently to life experiences. No two people experience exactly the same thing the same way. Not all people who are abused become abusers and vice versa.

You probably had some hurtful experiences that influenced your decision to offend. People who are basically well adjusted, have good self-esteem, communicate with and relate well to others, and are in touch with their feelings don't usually commit sex offenses. Some of the female offenders we've worked with have experienced situations that were hurtful or bordered on abuse, which created frustration, anger, feelings of abandonment, low self-esteem, a sense of loss, and so on. These situations included:

1) Having a totally dominating mother or father who didn't listen and made all the decisions

2) Being left out, used, or not appreciated while living with a parent and stepparent who had kids of his/her own (half brothers or sisters or step brothers or sisters)

3) Not having a mother or father, or having a mother or father who never came around

4) Having to grow up living with other relatives or in a foster or adoptive home because parent(s) could not raise you

5) Having one or both parents who were never available emotionally or weren't there when needed

6) Having a learning disability so school was harder, special classes were necessary, and/or you were limited in career opportunities

7) Having a speech or other type of impairment or disability

8) Being of a different race or religion than most of the people you were raised near

9) Having lost a close friend, pet, or family member through death, moving, or rejection

10) Feeling trapped in a no-win relationship or job

11) Feeling overwhelmed by responsibilities or debts

12) Feeling unappreciated

13) Having been unpopular and unliked in school

14) Being physically unattractive

These are a few reasons some people have problems that may result in behavior that either hurts themselves, others, or both. Can you think of some other situations that apply in your case?

In the next exercise, you have the opportunity to write down all of the smaller things that bother you, that you wish were different. Don't be afraid of sounding stupid. This is just for you. It is a healthy way of letting it all out.

Exercise 7. Airing Gripes

Part 1

First, just write down as many gripes as you can think of as fast as you can for ten minutes. Gripes can be things that are unfair, that you don't like, or that are frustrating, irritating, or making you feel crummy. They can be related to people, events, or just things that happen or are there. Do this as fast as you can. Don't elaborate. Use extra paper if necessary.

_____

_____

_____

_____

_____

_____

_____

_____

_____

_____

Part 2

In this section, look back at the exercise on abuse as well as at the first part of this exercise and pick out the various people who either abused or in some way caused you problems. Who were they? List them below.

_____

_____

_____

_____

_____

Now write a short note (just one or two sentences) to each telling them how you felt when they did what they did and why. For example, "Mom, I always felt worthless and like you thought I was stupid because I couldn't live up to your career expectations of me," or "Big Brother, I felt so uncomfortable, powerless, and stupid when you did those sexual things to me."

_____

_____

_____

_____

_____

_____

_____

_____

_____

Look over your list of gripes and the people involved. Can you discuss the abuses and gripes directly with the person who caused them? Often people are afraid to, afraid of what that person will think of them, afraid of being abused again (or worse), or afraid that person has forgotten. If you can sit down and talk these issues over, you will usually feel better. In some cases, however, the other person is not capable of listening. That is their problem. They are stuck in negative or hurtful behaviors. If the person is not available, won't listen, or is too dangerous to approach, talk some of these things over with someone else—your spouse, partner, a family member, a friend, or a counselor. It is good to get them out.

You may also want to write a longer letter to someone who has hurt you in some way. You don't have to give it to them. Just the exercise of writing the letter can help you get the feelings out. Every time you get those feelings out in a positive, healthy way, you will feel better. The letter below is a real letter written by a woman to her father who molested her.

Dear Dad,

I am writing to you because I want you to know what you put me through by molesting me. My life got shattered into tiny bits—a whole lifetime ruined—my whole self destroyed.

Being molested means having feelings that I'm not able to stand having sex with my husband or just not being able to love or touch my husband without it bringing back horrible memories. It means always being scared about getting betrayed again. It means being prejudiced or holding a grudge against the molester and everyone else who has molested. It means not ever wanting to see the molester again. It means having lots of mixed-up feelings, like being angry, sad, scared and hateful all at the same time. It means crying at night while thinking, "Why? Why did this happen to me?"

Molestation is a very scary thing, and I don't think I can ever forgive you for putting me through HELL by molesting me. It is something I will never forget.

Have you ever had any feelings like this? Has anyone ever done anything hurtful to you that you will never forget? Think hard. If you thought of something, did you list it? If not, go back and add it (them) in.

As a part of their therapy, many victims write letters like this one, sometimes sending them to their perpetrators, who are able to hear and understand what their victims are feeling. Some of these abusers are eventually able to talk through the issues, apologize, and demonstrate in their relapse-prevention plans how they are learning to change their harmful behaviors. Some abusers, however, never acknowledge the harm they did, which is very painful to the victims.

Some victims get enough help with their feelings so they feel "done" with the abuse and can go on with their lives. Some don't. But no one will ever be totally free of the effects of what their father, mother, family friend, relative, older brother, stranger, or other person did. A large percentage never feel able to fully trust their abuser(s) again, even though they may love that person and may be reconciled with him/her.

Often people who write and send letters to those who have hurt them don't get a reply. Remember three things as you work on the following exercise: 1) you are writing this letter to express *your* feelings, 2) you don't have to send it or, if you do send it, you don't need to get a reply for it to help, and 3) this letter is for *you*, a way to help yourself feel better, not for the other person.

Now is the time for you to write a longer letter to someone who hurt you. You can write it to your perpetrator(s) if you were abused, or to a parent, other family member, or friend who has let you down or treated you badly, or even to God.

Exercise 8. Letter to Someone Who Hurt Me

This letter may be as long or short as you want, but make sure to cover the topics listed below. (You may want to write more than one letter or a longer letter than the space allows you. Don't hesitate to use extra paper for this.)

1) What you are angry or hurt about or what bothers you (what the person[s] did)

2) What emotions you feel as a result of the abuse or other situation

3) What you think about the person(s) who caused the problem

4) How the abuse or other situation has affected how you act or behave

5) What you would like your abuser(s) (or whoever hurt you) to say or do, such as apologize, tell you why he/she acted that way, say something that shows he/she understands what you have gone through, etc.

Dear _____,

_____

_____

_____

_____

_____

_____

_____

_____

_____

_____

_____

_____

_____

_____

_____

_____

_____

_____

_____

_____

Signed: _____

Now think over what you wrote. How do you feel about the person(s) who hurt you? Will you forget about the hurt? Will you trust your abuser(s) again? How has your experience(s) affected your outlook on the world? How have your choices been affected by your experience(s)? Really think about this for a while. When you are victimized, you are forever changed by the experience. All experiences in life change us. Regardless of whether or not we get beyond the anger and hurt caused by the person(s) who hurt us, we will never quite be the same.

Some people can't seem to write their thoughts and feelings down very well or have trouble putting them into words. If you are one of those people, you may want to draw pictures of what happened to you, what you felt about it, what the abuser (or the person who treated you badly) looks like to you, and how you feel toward him/her.

Other women we have worked with have preferred to put these thoughts and feelings down in a song or poem. This is another good way to express them. One young person even constructed a horror house (like a doll house) that showed what happened to her and how she felt. Or you can talk your thoughts and feelings into a cassette recorder.

If someone committed an offense against you, it changed you. It was one of many factors that may have distorted your thinking, made you feel needy or bad about yourself, and contributed to your choice to commit or participate in a sexual offense. But you are still responsible for your choices. You can learn from your hurtful experiences and destructive acts. That is what this book is all about. That is what relapse prevention means. You can use your past experiences as learning tools—tools to make positive and thoughtful choices—and to help you to never repeat your offenses.

Getting in touch with the feelings behind your own victimizations and other painful experiences and situations is an important step toward change. If you know what you are feeling, you will be able to be more conscious of what other people are feeling at any given moment, so you can avoid hurting them.

Summary

You should have gained the following information from this chapter:

1) A better understanding of definitions of victimization and abuse and what actions they include.

2) Awareness of how and why some victims become sexual abusers.

3) More about the abuse you may have suffered.

4) Awareness of other acts, happenings, or situations that have bothered you.

5) Increased awareness of the impact and effects that the abuse and the other situations you experienced had upon your feelings, thoughts, and actions.

6) Some ways of dealing with your feelings about the people who hurt you and what they did.

7) Increased understanding that change and the power to make good choices are in your hands.

Chapter 4

Roles and Boundaries

Part of understanding who you are is understanding the different *roles* you play in life. A role is an identity you take on because of what you are doing in your life and in relation to someone else's life. A role has a lot to do with how other people see you. You may be a mother, a wife, a girlfriend, a friend, a daughter, a housekeeper, a babysitter, a worker in some other profession outside the home, an enemy, a leader in some endeavor or community group, a follower, a victim, a survivor, an abuser, a winner, or all of these. Some of these roles may be healthy ones, such as mother, while others may be unhealthy—such as a perpetual victim or an abuser.

Although many of the roles may overlap, each role has certain characteristics or functions and certain boundaries. Boundaries are like fences—they define where your responsibility or your reach stops and where others begin. For example, a mother functions as a nurturer, caregiver, helper, teacher, example, limit setter, and disciplinarian. But a mother is also expected to stay within certain boundaries. These boundaries include showing affection, but not being too close to her children. Or teaching by example that it's okay to express feelings, but not okay to take her frustrations out on other people. Or showing a child that there are consequences (like time outs or being sent to bed early or not getting special privileges) to breaking rules, but not by sexually, physically, or emotionally abusing him or her.

In a job, there might be boundaries between your responsibilities (you might be in sales, say) and those of a co-worker (he or she takes care of service calls), or between work and socializing on the job.

Roles and boundaries are not always easy to understand, but they are very important when it comes to making good choices. You can read more about boundaries after this exercise.

Exercise 9. The Roles You Play

In this exercise you will look at some of the roles you play in life.

Part I

Check off your most important roles on the next page. (Notice that some of these roles may be identical to the things you listed in chapter 2 that are important to you in your life.) At the end, add any roles that are not listed.

____ Mother	____ Follower	____ Teacher
____ Wife	____ Missionary	____ Friend
____ Partner	____ Spiritual guide	____ Babysitter
____ Lover	____ VIP (bigshot)	____ Girlfriend
____ Sister	____ Initiator	____ Role model
____ Daughter	____ Disciplinarian	____ Listener
____ Caretaker	____ Goof-off	____ Life of the party
____ Housekeeper	____ Comedian	____ Entertainer
____ Homemaker	____ Prima donna	____ Winner
____ Sexpot	____ Drudge	____ Decider
____ Wage-earner	____ Fuck-up	____ Sheep
____ Professional	____ Mediator	____ Team player
____ Victim	____ Peacemaker	____ Dreamer
____ Survivor	____ Troublemaker	____ Doer
____ Thriver	____ Loser	____ Control freak
____ Abuser	____ Winner	____ Organizer
____ Doormat	____ Sex object	____ Other roles
____ User	____ Tomboy	_____
____ Motivator	____ Oddball	_____
____ Leader	____ Loner	

Now circle all of the roles which you believe are healthy ones, and put an X through those that are not healthy. Also put a line under any of the roles you would like to adopt. What is keeping you from taking that role(s)? Discuss this with your group and therapist. Write down the steps you could do to take that role(s).

Roles are not set in stone. You have the power to change most of them by exercising your ability to choose. As you learned earlier in this book, to choose wisely it is important to figure out the likely consequences of each of the choices that you make. For example, you may want to get out of the wife role (at times, most married women do), but if you did that, you might lose your relationship altogether—a consequence you might not want. You might be happier adjusting that role so it fits you better. It's not necessarily a wife's role to do all the housework, for example, or to cook all the meals, or to do all the childcare. Sit down with your spouse or partner and talk about what would make that role more pleasurable. Can you share certain tasks? Is your spouse or partner willing to modify his/her roles too in order to accommodate your needs?

Part 2

Now it is time to look at the women in our world, past or present, that you most admire—your role models. Who are they? The women listed below are all famous, although you may not know who many of them are. They come from different generations, different cultures, and have different claims to fame. If you haven't heard of some of the women listed below or what they have done, ask your group or therapist. If they don't know, look the names up on the Internet or in the library. Discuss why they are famous and what they have done.

Select at least eight of the women below and/or add the names of your own role models. In the space beside their names, briefly write why you admire them.

Oprah Winfrey _____

Britney Spears _____

Laura Bush _____

Hillary Clinton _____

Madonna _____

Natalie Cole _____

Eleanor Roosevelt _____

Joan of Arc _____

Marie Curie _____

Gloria Steinem _____

Susan B. Anthony _____

Margaret Thatcher _____

Ellen Degeneres _____

Georgia O'Keefe _____

Rosa Parks _____

Helen Keller _____

Kristi Yamaguchi _____

Anna Freud _____

Julia Child _____

Julia Roberts _____

Queen Latifah _____

Golda Meier _____

Dolly Parton _____

Billie Jean King _____

Sojourner Truth _____

Lily Tomlin _____

Frida Kahlo _____

Jackie Kennedy _____

Aretha Franklin _____

Maya Angelou _____

Maria Tallchief _____

Shirley Chisholm _____

Sandra Day O'Connor _____

Ellen Ochoa _____

Isabel Peron _____

Marilyn Monroe _____

Jacqueline Joyner-Kersee _____

Katie Couric _____

Martina Navratilova _____

Princess Diana _____

Madeleine Albright _____

Selena _____

Wilma Mankiller _____

Indira Gandhi _____

Cleopatra _____

Suzanne Mubarak _____

Your mother _____

Your grandmother _____

Other female family member—who? _____

Others _____

_____

_____

Is there anything you can do to be more like the women you admire? Write some things you can do.

_____

_____

_____

Pick one thing that is within your abilities and do it, or start to do it. You don't have to become a Supreme Court Justice like Sandra Day O'Connor did, or a famous, talented athlete. But you can think through and make more reasoned decisions like O'Connor did while she was a justice, or improve your fitness and skill like Martina Navratilova or Billie Jean King, or perhaps become more giving like Oprah.

Boundaries are limits or borders. People have boundaries—borders we place on behaviors. You can think of them as fences whose purpose is to keep others out of areas that can hurt you or keep you out of areas where you don't belong, places that hurt others.

Boundaries, like roles, can be both healthy and unhealthy. If, for example, you have insufficient boundaries or no boundaries at all, people can take advantage of you, or use and abuse you. On the other hand, if you fence yourself in too tightly to be sure you can't be hurt, you may not be able to develop healthy relationships.

There are all kinds of boundaries. Some boundaries have to do with space. Everybody has their own space bubble, an area around them that they don't want people to enter. Has anyone ever gotten so close when they were talking to you that you felt uncomfortable? They got into your personal space bubble, violating your space boundary. Other people don't like to be touched. If you touch them in certain ways, you are violating their touch boundaries. And some people have speech boundaries. They are offended by certain words you may use.

Remember that boundaries can be things you do as well as things you don't do.

Talk over your answers with your group and/or your counselor.

Exercise 10. Personal Space

One of the easiest boundaries to understand is "personal space," the "bubble" you read about above. You will need a tape measure for this exercise, either the fabric kind used for sewing or the metal kind used in carpentry. In your treatment group pair off with someone or with your counselor. Stand six feet apart. Walk toward each other until one of you begins to feel uncomfortable, then stop. Measure how far apart you are. Write down whether it was you or the other person who first felt uncomfortable and the distance at which you stopped.

Distance: _____

Participant who stopped first: _____

Now begin walking toward each other again from that point until the other person feels uncomfortable, then stop. Measure the distance and write it down along with the person's name who felt uncomfortable.

Distance: _____

Participant: _____

Talk over the results with your group members or your counselor. How different were the distances for each person? What difference would it make if the other person was male or female, closer or further away? If the other person was a teenager or a child? Why?

Everyone has different boundaries in different areas and with different people, depending on the relationships of the people and society's rules. It is important to be sensitive to the people's various personal boundaries—the person whose boundary is broken or violated will feel uncomfortable and will either move away (if he or she can) or will not want to give you what you want. Children are in a special category because they don't know much about boundaries or personal space yet—their boundaries are not yet formed, so it is pretty easy to violate those boundaries. And because in our society children don't have much power, it is hard for them to get grown ups to pay attention to their boundaries.

Roles and boundaries can also be tied together. Unhealthy roles hurt you or others by violating not only your victim's boundaries but by destroying your healthy roles. When you committed or participated in a sexual offense, you broke the boundaries of your victim(s) and the boundaries of your role. For example, if you were a babysitter and you molested the children you were sitting for, you broke your babysitter-role boundary of caring for children so they would come to no harm, and you broke the children's roles as being the ones cared for, and instead did things to them that hurt them.

When you committed or participated in a sexual offense, you were unaware of the boundaries because you were detached from or had shut down your own feelings, you were expressing painful feelings in a hurtful way without thinking about boundaries, or you were so stuck in a victim or codependent role that you didn't stop someone else from violating boundaries. Becoming more aware of roles and boundaries can help you stop yourself from overstepping the boundaries of others.

Part 1

In this part of the exercise, we are going to look at some of your healthy roles from exercise 9. List four of them below. What are the boundaries that go with these healthy roles? A "breach" is a place where a wall or fence or boundary has been broken. What would be a breach of these roles? Write them down next to the role. For example, if your role is that of a "teacher," the boundary is not to go beyond instructing the persons you teach about the subject you are supposed to be teaching. A breach of the role would be to get romantically or overly emotionally involved with a student. More specifically, if part of your role as a "mother-teacher" is to instruct your child about sex, the role boundary is to verbally give the appropriate information. The breach would be to physically demonstrate sexuality on the child. Remember that boundaries can be things you do as well as things you don't do.

Now it's your turn to do the exercise.

1) Healthy Role _____

Boundary _____

Breach of Boundary _____

_____

2) Healthy Role _____

Boundary _____

Breach of Boundary _____

_____

3) Healthy Role _____

Boundary _____

Breach of Boundary _____

_____

4) Healthy Role _____

Boundary _____

Breach of Boundary _____

_____

Part 2

Now pick out four of your unhealthy roles from exercise 9 and write down how they violate either your own or someone else's boundary. For example, if your unhealthy role is "control freak," the healthy boundary is to control only your own behavior. If you are controlling the actions of others, you are violating their boundaries of autonomy or self-control.

1) Unhealthy Role _____

Boundary _____

Breach of Boundary _____

_____

2) Unhealthy Role _____

Boundary _____

Breach of Boundary _____

_____

3) Unhealthy Role _____

Boundary _____

Breach of Boundary _____

_____

4) Unhealthy Role _____

Boundary _____

Breach of Boundary _____

_____

Part 3

This part of the boundary exercise will give you the opportunity to determine if a boundary has been broken. Complete the questions, then discuss your answers with your group and/or therapist.

1) Wilma was angry at her neighbor, so she got right up close to the neighbor's face and started yelling at her. Did Wilma break the neighbor's boundary?_____

If so, in what way?

_____

_____

2) Elena's goddaughter came over for a visit. Elena gave the child a big hug. Did she violate the child's boundary? _____

   If so, in what way?

   _____

3) Karen hired a neighbor teen to babysit her three-year-old. She told the babysitter to do her dishes, make the beds, and clean the entire house. Did she violate any boundary of the babysitter? _____

   If so, in what way?

   _____

   _____

4) Althea, an adult, went to a local fast-food place where teenagers would hang out. She saw her fifteen-year-old nephew Bill there with his friends. She surprised him by giving him a big kiss on the mouth. Did she violate any of his boundaries? _____

   If so, in what way?

   _____

   _____

5) Martha was a junior-high-school teacher. She invited one of her students to go to the movies and out to dinner with her. Did she violate any boundaries? _____

   If so, what?

   _____

   _____

   Would it make any difference if the student's mother gave Martha permission? _____

   Why or why not?

   _____

   _____

   Would it make any difference if she took two or three students, instead of just one? _____

   Why or why not?

   _____

   _____

6) Carrie was drinking at a local bar. One of the bartenders, who was wearing a partly unbuttoned shirt, was really sexy. Carrie couldn't resist running her hands down the bare part of his chest. Did she violate any boundaries? _____

If so, what?

_____

_____

Would it make any difference if she was tipsy? _____

Why or why not?

_____

_____

7) Nana and Albert were madly in love. They started French kissing on a crowded bus. Did they violate any boundaries? _____

If so, whose? Why or why not?

_____

_____

8) Carla and Karen are lesbian friends. They ran into each other on the street and hugged. Did they violate any boundaries? _____

Why or why not?

_____

_____

Would it make any difference if they were heterosexual? _____

Why or why not?

_____

_____

9) Josie is nineteen. Her 14-year-old neighbor invites her over to see his new dog. She can tell he has a crush on her because he keeps sidling up to her and putting his arm around her shoulder. She decides to give him a treat by letting him fondle her breasts. Did she violate any boundaries? _____

Why or why not?

_____

_____

10) The fourteen-year-old neighbor boy is always looking into Josie's window when she is trying to get dressed in the morning. She decides to give him a show, so she goes up to the window in the nude and does a sexy dance in front of it. Did she violate any boundaries? _____

Why or why not?

_____

_____

If the peeping neighbor was an adult, would it make a difference?_____

How?

_____

_____

11) Candace found her younger sister's diary and started reading funny sections of it to her friends. Did she violate any boundaries? _____

Why or why not?

_____

_____

12) Barbara was babysitting Michael, age six. He kept misbehaving, so she made him wear his older sister's dress and parade down the street in front of his friends. Did Barbara violate any boundaries of Michael's? _____

If so, in what way?

_____

_____

13) Glenda was babysitting her nine-year-old neighbor on a hot summer day. The child asked Glenda if they could cool off by taking a shower. Both of them took their clothes off and got into the shower together. Did Glenda violate any boundaries? _____

If so, how?

_____

Would it make any difference if the child was Glenda's brother? _____

Why or why not?

_____

_____

Would it make any difference if the family were nudists? _____

Why or why not?

_____

_____

14) Sarah was working as a waitress. She accidentally spilled some cream on a male customer's pants. She took a wad of paper napkins and tried to mop up the mess on his lap. Is this a boundary violation? _____

Why or why not?

_____

_____

15) Nadine was crazy about her cousin's husband. She saw him in the park, ran over, and gave him a sexy tongue kiss. Is this a boundary violation? _____

If so, whose and why?

_____

_____

Summary:

You learned in this chapter:

   1) What roles are

   2) Which roles in your life are positive or negative

   3) How unhealthy roles can harm you and contribute to offending

   4) Who your own role models are

   5) What boundaries are

   6) How much "personal space" you feel comfortable with

   7) What a break or breach of boundary is and how it leads to offending

Chapter 5

Self-talk, Choices and Chains

The choices we all make begin with thoughts and feelings. When you feel good about yourself, you are more likely to make good, healthy choices with positive outcomes. When your self-esteem is low and you feel bad about yourself, you are more likely to make unhealthy choices and decisions that result in negative consequences, including hurting yourself or others or committing a sex offense.

There is always a conversation going on inside our minds. You catch your reflection in a store window and think to yourself, "You are looking good today, girl!" That's self-talk. Self-talk can be either positive or negative—it can help you feel better or worse, happy, angry, grateful, gracious or resentful. When someone bumps into you with her cart in the grocery store, what you say to yourself about it shapes how you choose to respond. If you think, "That woman ran into me on purpose!" you will feel differently and choose a different response than if you think, "She's so distracted with her little boy, I'm sure she didn't mean it."

Thoughts (such as self-talk) and feelings are linked together to shape the choices you make. You could picture them as the links of a necklace chain. How you think about yourself and others and what you say to yourself is linked to how you feel. How you feel is linked to what you choose to do.

When you feel hungry, your self-talk is, "I need to get something to eat." Then you choose an action as a consequence (remember those?) of your feeling hungry and your self-talk: you get out some bread and tuna fish to make a sandwich. You sit down and eat, and the next consequence is that you feel full. Feeling and thinking linked to choosing an action that had a consequence: a Choice Chain.

Exercise 12. Choice Chains

Think of three every-day actions that are part of your routine, for example, choosing what to wear, or what music to listen to on the stereo. List them below.

1. _____

2. _____

3. _____

Start with the action (example: putting on a blouse). What was your self-talk? (Example: "I want to look good today," or "It's going to be hot, so I'd better wear something with short sleeves."). List at least one self-talk statement for each action.

1. _____

2. _____

3. _____

What were you feeling either just before your self-talk or right after it?

1. _____

2. _____

3. _____

You have just gone through a feeling-thought (self-talk)-choice/action chain from end to beginning. If you rearrange the steps, you will see the chain the way it happened, from beginning (feeling) to end (choice/action).

Your offending behavior results from the same kind of choice chain, but it usually starts when you feel bad, sad, or mad. You might say to yourself, "I'm crummy, no good for anything but sex." And that feeling and self-talk might link to your choice to approach a child or someone else who cannot give consent for sexual contact. When your choice chain leads to offending behavior, it is called an "offense chain." You will learn more about offense chains and changing self-talk later in this book.

The best thing about choice chains is that you can change the links. When you change your self-talk, that can change your feelings, and together those changes will result in your choosing a different, more positive action with a better consequence.

It's not always easy to catch your own self-talk. Usually the first clue is a feeling. In your offense chain, something happens or someone says something to you and you feel angry or resentful or hurt or lonely. Whatever the person said, it reminded you of a feeling.

For example, Sherry's friend Delilah told her, "You're never going to get a boyfriend." Sherry felt hopeless and lonely. It reminded her of what her mother used to tell her and clicked right in with Sherry's old self-talk. Sherry didn't want to feel hopeless and depressed. She decided she would go get someone to be her boyfriend—and she knew just how and exactly who—and then she would feel better. The "who" was the 14-year-old who mowed the lawn, and the "how" was she would invite him in for lemonade and begin touching him and telling him how strong he was and offer him sex.

Sherry could have changed her self-talk to link to a more positive choice, but only if she could slow down the process enough to realize how Delilah's comment started the chain.

Urges and PIGs: Linking the Beginning to the End

Just like a necklace links together to make a circle, many choice chains also link together at the beginning and end to create a circle, a repeating pattern. Your offense chain is one of those. If it starts when you feel bad or sad, you probably will end up feeling bad or sad about what you did in being sexual with a child or another adult who could not consent, and that creates the circle chain of choice.

There's another important part of the offense chain to look at, the Problem of Immediate Gratification, which we call the "PIG." Think of how it feels when you want something, and you want it NOW! That luscious chocolate cake in the bakery window just about calls your name, even though you're on your way home to make dinner. The shoes that would exactly go with the outfit you bought last week, you absolutely have to have them, so you duck into the store, even though you'll be late for work, and you'll be putting them on your almost-maxed-out credit card.

When satisfying a desire right away—chocolate, shoes, sex—is more important than considering the consequences, that's a problem. The Problem of Immediate Gratification is part of the energy that drives your offense chain into its circular pattern. It takes the form of an "urge," a feeling that you need to do something in particular.

Many urges start with emotional needs that are translated into physical urges. For example, when you are feeling bored and lonely, you may have the urge to eat, even if you aren't physically hungry. You may have eaten just an hour before, but you crave some cookies. You remember the pleasure cookies gave you in the past and are attempting to capture that pleasure again. You don't even think about the negative consequences—how you will gain unwanted weight or spoil your appetite for dinner. You just grab more and more of them and wolf them down.

This pressure to satisfy an emotional need is the Problem of Immediate Gratification. The PIG also applies to sexual urges. If you have been feeling some painful emotions, such as depression or anger, you may crave the sexual act you committed because you remember the pleasure or release it gave you.

For example, people were always making fun of Mari. She felt depressed, unliked, and stupid. She was at home one day, when a young neighbor child came over and asked if he could use the bathroom because his mom was late returning from work and he couldn't get into his house. Mari showed him where her bathroom was. The boy came back and told Mari he needed help unzipping his pants. Mari went into the bathroom with him and helped him get his pants down. She had the urge to touch his penis. This is the PIG. If Mari had done a similar offense before to try to feel better, she is more likely repeat the behavior. The PIG fits its name. It is a greedy animal. It wants to be fed over and over again. The more you give in to it, the more the PIG comes back to bother you.

Sandy, a thirty-five-year-old woman whose boyfriend just dumped her, was feeling angry at him, lonely, unattractive, and incapable of maintaining a relationship. She thought that the fifteen-year-old boy doing her gardening was cute. She would always talk and laugh with him. This time she had the urge to have sex with him because she wanted to feel attractive and wanted. This is the PIG. She had an urge and wanted to satisfy it. She didn't think about the consequences. She took all of her clothes off, put on a satin robe, and invited him into the house for a drink. She also gave him some pot to smoke with her and then began to arouse him by putting her hands on his thigh and letting her robe fall open. She gave in to the PIG and wound up going to jail for molesting the boy.

In the next exercise, we will look at some needs that people try to satisfy by offending, and find better choices to satisfy those needs.

Exercise 13. Satisfying Needs

Part 1

Cover up the second part of this exercise. (Come on, don't cheat!) We want you to think for yourself. On the following lines, write down what needs you think you were trying to satisfy when you committed or participated in your sex offense(s). Brainstorm as many as you can.

_____

_____

_____

_____

_____

_____

_____

_____

_____

_____

_____

_____

_____

Part 2

This exercise might be a bit of a stretch for you, because you'll need to think beyond what you already did and imagine a healthier way of dealing with your emotional needs. In the left-hand column below, we have listed some of the common needs that female sex offenders are trying to fill when they engage in unhealthy behaviors or participate in or commit sex offenses.

In the right-hand column, list ways that you have tried to meet these needs that were unhealthy for you and/or harmed someone else and got you into trouble.

In the right-hand column, fill in other, healthier ways that could and/or would fill those needs if you had them. Include specific actions or activities you might do. For example, if your need was for power and control, maybe one of your ways of satisfying this need would be to go bowling. List at least three alternatives for each need.

Needs Behind Sex Offenses / Unhealthy Behaviors	Negative Ways I've Met This Need	Better Ways of Satisfying Them
Caring, connection, or love (feeling lonely)	1)_____ 2)_____ 3)_____	1)_____ 2)_____ 3)_____
To be looked up to, admired, respected, or capable (feeling inadequate)	1)_____ 2)_____ 3)_____	1)_____ 2)_____ 3)_____
To feel whole or that your life has some purpose (feeling empty inside)	1)_____ 2)_____ 3)_____	1)_____ 2)_____ 3)_____
To please a special person in your life (feeling dependent on that person)	1)_____ 2)_____ 3)_____	1)_____ 2)_____ 3)_____

To release or vent anger	1)_____	1)_____
(feeling frustrated or	2)_____	2)_____
angry)	3)_____	3)_____

Power or control	1)_____	1)_____
(feeling helpless or out	2)_____	2)_____
of control)	3)_____	3)_____

Excitement (feeling bored	1)_____	1)_____
or that life is dull)	2)_____	2)_____
	3)_____	3)_____

Sexual satisfaction or to	1)_____	1)_____
fill a sexual fantasy	2)_____	2)_____
(feeling sexual)	3)_____	3)_____

Other need	1)_____	1)_____
(one of your own)	2)_____	2)_____
	3)_____	3)_____

Other need	1)_____	1)_____
(one of your own)	2)_____	2)_____
	3)_____	3)_____

Exercise 14. Beginning My Offense Chain

Look at Sandy's story above and fill in the offense chain below. At the end or the bottom of her offense chain is what she did to fifteen-year-old Marcus: she molested him by oral sex and then intercourse. Fill in the rest of Sandy's chain. Imagine what she might have thought to herself at each step, and write that down above the action she took. The top of the chain would be Sandy's boyfriend dumping her, and her feelings about it.

_____

_____

_____

_____

_____

_____

_____

_____

_____

Now it's your turn. Fill in your own offense chain as far as you understand it right now. In the space below or on a separate piece of paper, write your offense at the bottom ("molesting a child" or "assaulting an unconscious adult" or whatever you did). Then write what you did or thought or felt just before that on the line above it, until you get to the feeling or event that started you on this path. If you are having trouble thinking about each step, pair up with another person in your group to ask each other, "What did you do (or think or feel) before that?" Or ask for help from your counselor.

_____

_____

_____

_____

_____

_____

_____

_____

_____

Now you can begin to see that offending is still all about choices and consequences. Each step you took was a consequence of the step before it. Each step was the result of a choice you made about how you felt or thought and what you would do.

Risky Decisions in Disguise

There are a few more parts to your offense chain. The first is called "Seemingly Unimportant Decisions" (SUDs). Those are the decisions you make that at first glance don't seem to be connected to your offense chain. These everyday decisions seemed reasonable, but were risky because they placed you in a potentially offending situation.

Sandy, for example, made a seemingly unimportant decision when she thought, "I'm having a bad day, so I'll just get into my robe and maybe take a bath." In reality, she knew that Marcus, the fifteen-year-old gardener, was working outside, but she convinced herself that her decision to be naked had nothing to do with her eventual goal of having sex with him.

Can you think of any SUDs you made in your offense chain?

Exercise 15. SUDs

Go back to the previous exercise and circle any decision or thought that might be a Seemingly Unimportant Decision. Perhaps you offered to babysit in an emergency, or let a child sleep in your bed after a bad dream. Any decision that moved you closer to having an opportunity to offend could be a SUD.

One more part of your offense chain is figuring out "Risky Situations," the places, people, feelings, and thoughts that shaped your decisions toward offending.

Looking again at Sandy's situation, it seems clear that being depressed and lonely put her at risk to make some bad decisions. Having a relationship break up is a risky situation. And certainly, inviting Marcus into the house set up a risky situation.

Risky situations don't have to lead to offenses, but you'll need to be able to recognize them and consciously change your decisions to get out of them. Two techniques you'll learn more about in part II are Avoidance and Escape.

Thinking Errors

The last major part of your offense chain that we're going to discuss in this section is "Thinking Errors." Nearly everyone uses thinking errors at one time or another, especially when we're trying to make ourselves feel better about a decision that we know is questionable or just plain wrong.

Janet was depressed. Her girlfriend had canceled out on a movie date, leaving her with nothing to do but watch TV. She walked through the kitchen and saw the three batches of brownies her roommate Taylor had baked for the Community Center bake sale the next day. "Wow, that's a lot of brownies," she thought. "Nobody will miss it if I just have one. I'm so depressed, I deserve something nice, and besides, I contributed to the groceries that went into these."

She took a brownie and watched a half-hour comedy on TV. She had spilled a few crumbs on the couch, so she went back into the kitchen for the dustpan and brush—and took another brownie. After the next program, she went to wash her hands, and thought, "Taylor must have wanted us to sample these, since she left them out here," and took another brownie.

Janet was using thinking errors to *justify* every decision she made to eat a brownie that wasn't hers. She *minimized* the effect of her taking the first brownie ("nobody will miss it"). She felt *entitled* to take the brownie ("I deserve it") because she felt depressed and because all members of the household put money into the grocery budget. She was *projecting* her own desires onto her roommate ("Taylor must have wanted us to sample these") to *rationalize* her decision to keep eating the bake sale goodies.

Those are a few of the most common thinking errors. Although eating someone else's bake sale brownies isn't a serious offense, sex offenders use the same thinking errors to shape their decisions to have sex with a child or an adult who won't or can't legally consent.

Exercise 16. Thinking Errors in My Offense

Go back and reread your offense chain. Over on the side of the page, Write down at least one thought for each of the steps and decisions you made. Look at your thoughts. Put a check mark beside each one that might be a thinking error. Talk over your list in your group or with your counselor.

We will look at your offense in more detail in part II when we discuss how you can step in at any link in your offense chain and change your thinking, feelings, decisions, and actions for a more positive, offense-free outcome.

Summary

You can now:

Identify your self-talk.

Recognize the Problem of Immediate Gratification.

Identify your emotional needs that led to offending.

List many of the steps in your offense chain.

Recognize risky situations.

Explain Seemingly Unimportant Decisions.

List some thinking errors you used in your offense.

Chapter 6

Chains Turn into Cycles

When the same pattern runs over and over again, it is called a cycle. You might have learned about the water cycle in school: water evaporates from the land, lakes, rivers, and the ocean; in the air, the water vapor condenses into clouds; when the weather is right, the clouds pour rain back onto the land, where it trickles back into the lakes, rivers, and the ocean; and the cycle starts again.

The cycle you are dealing with here is called an offense cycle because your pattern of offending can repeat itself. We talked in a previous chapter about how links make a chain that can join together into a circle, like a necklace. A circle is one way to describe the shape of a cycle. You just keep going around and around doing the same things unless you become aware of each of the stages in the cycle and take action to change your thoughts, feelings, and behaviors at each step.

But before you turn your offense chain from the last chapter into your offense cycle, let's look at how offenses generally occur. People commit offenses because they don't know how else to deal with their emotional needs. It's as if you have only one kitchen tool in your drawer, or one color of crayon in the box. No matter what is happening, you only have a spatula or a blue crayon to deal with it. This situation is called having "inadequate coping resources."

What do we mean by that? When a difficult or painful circumstance occurs or you have unfulfilled needs, you have to somehow handle or "cope" with them. If you don't have a whole drawer full of tools to productively deal with them, your coping resources are inadequate. For example, if something triggers a painful emotion, such as frustration, anxiety, inadequacy, anger, fear, loneliness, or depression, you may act on it in an unhealthy, destructive way.

It is important to look carefully at how this works. Just as pulling a gun's trigger fires it, emotional triggers fire you up into a painful emotional state. Emotional triggers are events or happenings that "set you off." For example, for an African-American, being called "nigger" by a white person may be a trigger for anger or rage. Most people's anger is triggered when they feel put down, used, betrayed, frustrated, not treated fairly, or disrespected.

Without more tools or possibilities to help you cope, you are likely to do something that either harms you or harms someone else. We call harming yourself "acting in," and it includes substance abuse (alcohol or prescription or street drugs), cutting or injuring yourself physically, suicide, or similar self-destructive behaviors. We call harming others "acting out," an aggressive response toward others. Aggressive responses fall into two categories: coercive, which results in child molestation, or violent, which results in assaults, rape, or homicide. See the diagram below for a clearer picture of this pattern.

How Your Feelings and Choices Lead to Offenses

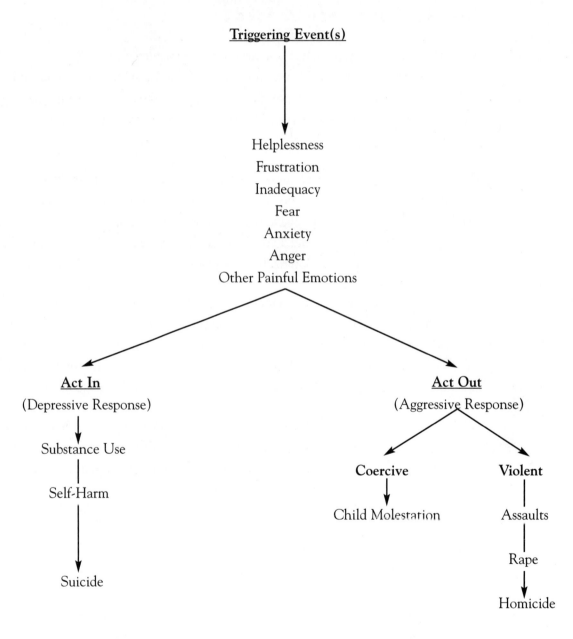

If you have thought the painful emotions through and have appropriate strategies for dealing with them (good coping strategies), you will not follow either of these dysfunctional paths. You will not reoffend.

Let's look at the offense cycle. You will see that your acting-out and acting-in responses, how you feel, and what you do afterward have a generally repetitive pattern. The diagram below shows how this happens.

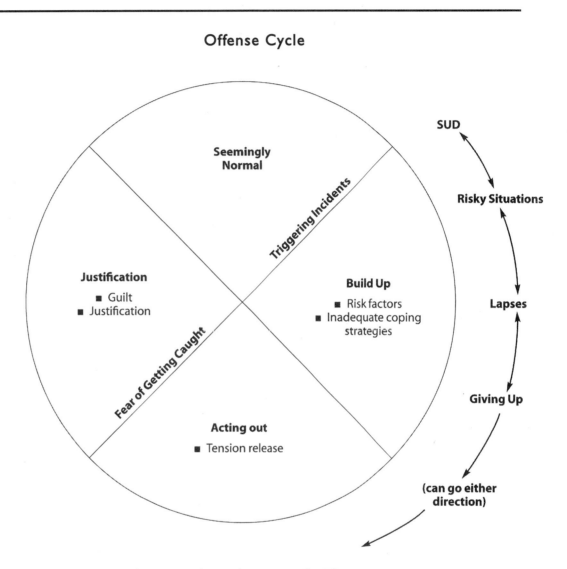

Offense Cycle

You can see how you might seemingly go along normally. Then one or more triggering incidents occur. These could be things like your husband having an affair, your girlfriend breaking up with you, your children getting into trouble with the law, losing your job, flunking an examination, having your best friend betray your confidences, or a million other happenings that cause you to feel painful emotions.

If these painful emotions, which we shall call "risk factors," build up, and you lack planned methods for taking care of yourself, you could act out in numerous destructive ways, including molesting or physically abusing your own or other people's children or attacking either the person(s) that hurt you or somebody else—any way that helps you to release the emotional tension and pain. This is why it is so important to identify your triggers and risk factors. If you are unaware of them or stuff them down and refuse to deal with them, you are much more likely to reoffend or commit some other type of destructive act. And if you don't have planned, positive ways of coping with them when they arise, you are also much more likely to act in a negative way.

Once you commit the destructive act, fear of getting caught and guilt about what you did always follow. You may also rationalize and justify what you did so you won't feel so bad about yourself. It is common to explain away your behavior with thinking errors and distortions such as, "It's okay because the same thing happened to me," or "The victim wanted me to do it," or "It won't hurt the victim. He/she will forget about it." It is only natural to try to make yourself feel better. Your guilt and fear begin to fade away, and you try to put your offense behind you.

After the offense, you may go back to "business as usual," but underneath you still feel bad about yourself, guilty about the offense, and afraid of what will happen to you. Do you remember feeling that way? Once you feel somewhat better, you seemingly go along normally again until something else triggers those painful emotions.

Arlene followed that pattern. Arlene's husband gambled away all their rent money, then left her for someone else. She was feeling really depressed, worried about being evicted, furious at her husband, and very helpless, since she had three children to feed plus a new baby on the way. She was also feeling very ugly and unlovable due to her pregnancy. The only light in her life was her daughter Adriana. Adriana was her angel, a sweet, helpful child of eight, who gave her unconditional love and affection.

One night when Arlene was feeling particularly desperate, Adriana jumped out of bed in her nightgown and began hugging her mother and telling her everything would be okay. Arlene stroked her daughter's hair and back, holding her close. She was feeling loved and soothed. Slowly, she began reaching under the nightgown to touch her daughter's soft skin, eventually working her way around from her back to her thighs and then touching her daughter's vaginal area. It felt good and warm and exciting. The tension she had been feeling ceased.

But then Arlene began to get frightened, realizing that what she was doing was wrong, fearful she would be caught and her children would be taken away from her. She told her daughter not to say anything. She felt guilty the whole next day. Then she began justifying what she did, saying to herself, "I didn't start it; Adriana came to me. Besides, I didn't hurt her. I was just showing her how much I love her. No harm was done."

After that, things went back to normal. Arlene's problems were relatively manageable. Nothing bad happened for a while. Arlene found a boyfriend who moved in and supported them. She had her baby. All seemed fine until she caught her boyfriend cheating on her. Then the whole cycle started again.

For someone who helped a partner sexually abuse someone, the cycle may be a little different. Often the painful emotions may include such things as feeling needy, having poor self-esteem, and being afraid that a partner will leave you if you don't go along with the acting-out behaviors. Then once the sexual act is completed, there may be a sense of relief that it is over, that you can go on with your life with that partner. But the same fear of getting caught, guilt, and justifications come into play.

Sometimes, in either type of situation—with a partner or solo—you may feel that the sexual pleasure and excitement of the risk you are taking make the abuse worthwhile. Life becomes better. But that's because you have detached from your painful feelings and rationalized or justified your behavior to yourself. If this was how you felt, look at it more closely. How did you feel when your partner initially encouraged or made you participate with him/her? During? Afterward? How did you feel when you acted alone—before, during, and afterward?

The following exercise will help you look at all of these factors in your offense cycle.

Exercise 17. My Offense-Cycle Elements

Think the following questions over carefully and answer as best you can. Notice that you have to separate out what you were thinking and what you were feeling. Feelings are usually adjectives like "lonely," "happy," "sad," "anxious," "angry," etc. (Write down both the healthy and unhealthy thoughts and the pleasant and unpleasant/painful feelings you were having in each situation.)

Before My Offense:

What was going on in my life?

1) At home: _____

_____

2) At work: _____

_____

3) In school: _____

_____

4) With my relationships: _____

_____

5) With my family: _____

_____

6) Pleasures: _____

_____

7) Problems or frustrations: _____

_____

8) Other important factors: _____

_____

What was I *thinking* as I decided to take the next step toward my illegal sex act?

_____

_____

What I was *feeling* as I decided to take the next step toward my illegal sex act?

_____

_____

During My Offense:

What was I *thinking* while the sexual act was happening?

_____

_____

What was I *feeling* while the sexual act was happening?

_____

_____

After My Offense:

What did I think to myself right after the offense was over?

_____

_____

How did I feel right after the offense was over?

_____

_____

What did I do right after the offense was over?

_____

_____

What did I think about my offense the next day?

_____

_____

What did I feel about my offense the next day?

_____

_____

Did things ever seem to go back to normal? _____

If not, what seemed different?

_____

_____

What did I feel when I got arrested or caught?

_____

_____

Notice that one of the main differences between the first offense chain you learned (which is to the right of the diagram of the cycle) and the offense cycle is that what happens after the offense is committed has been added.

Also note how the offense cycle fits with the reoffense chain. If you don't make a seemingly unimportant decision that places you in a risky/dangerous situation, you will not have the need to offend. So remember: even if something triggers the build-up of risk factors, and even if you don't usually cope very well, you can't reoffend if you are not in a dangerous situation or if you escape from that situation before reoffending. (Of course to make doubly sure you won't reoffend, it's better to keep yourself safe *and* do something positive about your painful emotions.) And notice, when everything is going along normally, how easy it is to put yourself into a dangerous situation. You have to be aware and prepared on both fronts.

Some offenders who are in treatment want to believe that they will never, never offend again, no matter what. But if they haven't gained an awareness of their triggers and emotions and learned positive ways of dealing with them, they can offend again just as easily as they did before. What you are learning here is something you need to apply forever.

For others who have fantasized and committed sexual offenses over and over again, offending can sometimes feel like an addiction. These repetitive offenses, typically exposing themselves (flashing), making obscene phone calls, and peeping in windows, are often triggered by feelings of anxiety, frustration, boredom, or helplessness. Even child molesters who feel sexually and emotionally attracted to children rather than adults often give in to their desires when they feel helpless, hopeless, frustrated, and lonely. So being very aware of and having positive coping methods for your triggers, emotions, thinking, and acting will be critical to keeping yourself from reoffending.

Another Link: Giving Up

There is one more stage in your offense cycle to learn about that is most important for you to understand so you will not reoffend. That stage is when you realize you're about to do something wrong, but you just give up and go ahead anyway. The fancy name for this stage is the "Abstinence Violation Effect."

Abstinence is staying away from doing something. Abstinence from food is what's going on when someone is doing extreme dieting or fasting. Abstinence from sex is being celibate.

Violation means breaking a rule. Effect is the way an action makes you feel.

Abstinence Violation Effect (AVE) is how you feel when you promised yourself not to do something, and then you get closer and closer to doing it, or maybe you already are beginning to do it, and instead of stopping, you give up and go ahead. You take three cookies when you're on a diet. You realize you're three miles over the speed limit on the highway and give up on your promise not to get any more tickets and go fifteen miles an hour over the limit.

In your offense cycle, you realize you have your hand on a child's thigh, and you see you're on your way toward more sexual touching, but you give up and think, "I've already gone this far, I might as well go all the way." An old phrase that expresses this thinking error is "In for a penny, in for a pound." In legal terms, it's a little like having the same penalties for being an accomplice as if you did the main crime.

In part II, we'll look more closely at the AVE.

Summary:

You can now:

Identify your triggers

Understand the difference between acting out and acting in

See how your offense chain becomes an offense cycle

Outline your offense cycle

Understand Abstinence Violation Effect

Chapter 7

Sex and Consent

You are in treatment because you participated in sexual behavior that involved someone who did not or could not give consent.

Sex is described in the dictionary as "the instinct or attraction drawing one [person] toward another, or its manifestation in sexual behavior." Sex involves your brain, all your physical senses, and your genitals.

As with other choices you make, the choice to have sex results in both positive and negative consequences. Positive consequences can include sexual release, good feelings, closeness, and (for adults who are ready to be parents) babies. Negative consequences can include babies (for people who don't want them or are not mature enough to be good parents), abortions, possible bad reputations, low self-esteem, and sexually transmitted diseases, such as herpes, syphilis, chlamydia, and HIV or AIDS. Some of the negative consequences can be prevented when both partners take responsibility by using birth control and a condom, or by carefully sterilizing any sex toys they might share with a partner.

In our society, sex is mixed up with everything else, used for different purposes, and combined with just about every possible subject in many different contexts. Advertisements use sex to sell perfumes, sodas, blue jeans, cars, and almost anything imaginable.

Sex, love, and intimacy are often confused. *Intimacy* is emotional closeness and familiarity with another person; *love* is great care for, and possibly a romantic attachment to, another person; *sex* is a physical act involving the arousal of genitalia. For most women who commit sex offenses, these tend to get all mish-mashed together in an unhealthy, less-than-wonderful way, but they are very different from one another. While you may experience all of them at the same time with the right person—which can be wonderful—it is possible to experience each separately.

Consent is permission or agreement. In a hospital, before you have surgery, you are required to sign a document giving your "informed consent." The document outlines all the known consequences, everything that could happen as a result of having the surgery. In relationships, few people ever write or sign an "informed consent" document. But there must be some understanding of what will happen. In a "consensual relationship," the participants understand that they will have sex together, that there will be emotional and physical consequences, that some consequences will be short-term and some might be long-term, and they agree to go ahead.

Someone who does not understand cannot give consent. A child does not understand the consequences of sex. Every state has a law defining when a child is old enough to understand the consequences of sex, the "age of legal consent." Typically in the United States, that age is sixteen, but different states use different ages.

Adults who are developmentally delayed may not be able to give legal consent if they don't understand about sex. Adults who are very drunk or drugged or unconscious or sleeping obviously cannot give consent. Using force or threats or lies to make someone participate in sexual activities means that there is no consent. Having sex without consent is a crime, a sex offense.

When adults consent to have sex together without being in a committed relationship, it is usually called "casual sex." Casual sex is what you may have already been involved in, sex just to have sex, just for orgasms, without caring about the other person. Casual sex may be physically pleasant, but it does not satisfy your needs for closeness and caring. If you are in a committed relationship, having casual sex with someone else means you are probably violating your significant other's trust. Frequent casual sex may mean that you have a problem with intimacy and/or were sexually abused.

Many women think they are in love, when they are really only in *lust*, or they look for intimacy through sexuality—which is usually a disappointment because all they wind up with is a sexual experience and no real closeness.

Meaningful and responsible sex involves caring about the other person's needs and well-being as much as you care about yourself. It involves a relationship of respect and trust. It allows both partners to share their feelings as well as their genitals. It requires consideration of the consequences. Responsible sex means using birth control and a condom.

Because this is so important, we'll say it again: when a person has a sexual experience (or helps another person have one) with someone who has not given his or her consent, or with someone who is underage and/or incapable of consenting, she has hurt someone and has committed a sex offense. Sex offenses are crimes. Children and developmentally disabled people are not legally, mentally, or emotionally capable of consenting. They are easily manipulated by someone older, or stronger, or in a position of authority. Similarly, persons who are drunk, drugged, or unconscious are not capable of consent, and sexual activity with them is a crime.

Some sex offenses don't even involve touching. Obscene phone calls, exposing one's genitals, peeping, taking non-consensual nude or sexy photos, showing pornography to a child, or viewing child pornography are sex offenses, just like the hands-on offenses, such as fondling the genitals of a child or having the child touch your breasts or vaginal area (molestation), forced intercourse (rape), intercourse with someone who has passed out, or oral copulation (mouth to genital contact) with a child or non-consenting adult.

Women who commit sex offenses are particularly likely to confuse sex with intimacy. Confusing sex with intimacy often happens when the women were molested themselves when they were young, felt some closeness during the sexual activity with the abusers, and mistakenly think having sex will bring them the closeness and caring they are looking for. But it doesn't. While the victim may feel some pleasurable bodily sensations, feelings of being used, powerless, or dirty combine with those feelings of pleasure. Not only does the offender not get the closeness she wants, but the victim is emotionally harmed.

When Isabel was a little child, her favorite uncle molested her. Although afterward she felt kind of dirty and used and that there must be something wrong with her that made him do it, she still really loved her uncle. She confused her feelings of closeness to him with her sexual experience.

When Isabel became an adult, she got married. But the marriage ended when her husband left her for another woman. She felt lonely and unloved. She worked as a juvenile hall counselor. One of her students, Eddy, a young boy of thirteen who came from an abusive broken home, really seemed to need love and attention. She listened to him, helped him with his schoolwork, and began taking him places when he was released. She let him stay over at her apartment. He really seemed to adore her. One day, she had him touch her breasts. She then had him pull down his pants and she rubbed his penis. She was trying to find the closeness she thought she had with her uncle. She didn't think about the effect it would have on Eddy, who was confused and hurt. She felt ashamed and guilty afterward and still felt lonely and unloved. Then she was arrested. She had acted out her need for intimacy and love in an inappropriate, illegal, sexual way with someone who could not understand and consent. She had confused love and intimacy with sex.

Ella, a middle-school teacher, was always extremely overweight as a teenager and adult. She never dated because no one could look beyond her physical size. She had no close friends, and she was lonely and looking for love. One of her students would stay after school and talk with her. She thought he seemed very mature for twelve. They began to go out to eat together, went to movies, and even threw water balloons at cars from the window of her apartment. She would kiss him goodbye, showing him how to use his tongue in kissing. She asked him if he would like to learn how to please her sexually. He said, "sure," so she taught him to suck her breasts. She convinced herself that they had a mature love relationship. But in reality she was exploiting a needy student who wasn't ready for sexual experiences and felt confused and used.

Power is another quality some women who sexually offend confuse with sex. This is particularly true of those who were molested or more violently sexually assaulted and felt helpless at the time. Consciously or subconsciously, they remember the power and control the offender had over them. When these women feel powerless or frustrated as teens or adults, they may want to gain control of somebody or something, just like the person who offended against them did. Women who sexually assault or molest someone who is weaker or younger, expose their genitals to a stranger, peep or make obscene phone calls, or participate in an aggressive sex offense often show this pattern. They misuse sex to try to satisfy their need for power.

Renée was attacked and raped when she was fifteen. She felt totally out of control and help-less during the incident. The rapist had all the power. Later on in life, Renée's relationship with her boyfriend seemed to be falling apart, she was in debt, and she had a coke habit that was bankrupting her. She felt completely powerless once again. She suggested to her boyfriend that they have sex with the two thirteen-year-old boys next door. They invited the boys over, gave them booze and pot, and then Renée had sex with the boys while her boyfriend mastur-bated. She felt powerful when she was able to control the boys. Although the boys seemed to enjoy the substances and sex, they were being damaged by both experiences. The experiences were not appropriate for their age. They began having problems relating to kids their own age, and they felt the same helplessness that Renée felt when she was raped. They started acting out, getting in trouble because of the anger and confusion they felt from the abuse.

Others misuse sex as a means of excitement—as a way of getting away from the boredom and humdrum parts of life. For example, Shirley was stuck at home with her three young children, all under five. Her husband always came home tired, and they never did anything fun. When her fifteen-year-old nephew came over to visit, she molested him because having sex with him was new and exciting. Once again, although she didn't force him to do anything, the inappropriate sexual contact caused him problems. He, too, felt confused, used, and different from his peers.

Still other women may misuse sex is as an outlet for anger. Nina was furious at her husband for going out and making her stay at home and babysit their eighteen-month-old baby. So she pinched, twisted, and hit the baby's penis. A sexual abuse victim herself with rape fantasies, she found herself sexually excited by what she was doing.

These are just a few of the ways offenders mix up sex with satisfying another emotional need. Can you figure out what was behind your misuse of sex? The next exercise will give you that opportunity. You may have more than one reason.

Exercise 18. Sex and Sex Offending

Part I

In this part of the exercise, you will be determining if sex is being misused or is dysfunctional and in what way. Note that sexual misuse is not necessarily a crime, and some things are crimes that are not necessarily dysfunctional. Make sure to discuss these with your group and/or therapist. Some items are not black or white. The idea is for you to really think about what you consider healthy or dysfunctional and why.

1) Sarita is very attractive and likes to be the center of attention. When she goes to church every Sunday, she wears sheer blouses and no bra. She finds it exciting that people stare at her. Is this a misuse of sex? _____

Why? _____

_____

What might her reasons be for flaunting herself this way?

_____

_____

How do you think the other people in church feel?

_____

_____

Do you think the men might feel differently than the women? _____

If so, how? _____

_____

2) Evelyn goes out every night to a local bar and brings men home to have sex. She never sees the same man more than one night. Is this a misuse of sex? _____

Why? _____

_____

What do you think she is looking for?

_____

_____

What negative effects might this behavior have on her?

_____

_____

3) Carla, who is sexually attracted to women, frequently goes to a local gay bar to meet women. She just talks with them and gets to know them. She has had sex only with partners with whom she has developed a close and caring relationship. Is this a misuse of sex? _____

Why? _____

_____

What do you think Carla is looking for?

_____

_____

4) When Antoinette was babysitting her sister's baby girl, she had the urge to feel the baby's soft skin. She rubbed the baby's chest and tummy and the baby cooed. Then she rubbed between the baby's legs. The baby continued to make noises like she was enjoying being touched. Was Antoinette's behavior wrong? _____

Why? _____

_____

Does it make a difference that the baby would be too young to remember what happened? _____

Why? _____

_____

Why might Antoinette have done this?

_____

_____

5) Tara was at a party where she got loaded on alcohol and pot. When she went into the bedroom to get her coat to leave, she saw a good looking guy passed out on the bed. He had loosened his belt and unbuttoned his pants. She was curious, so she unzipped his pants and pulled his penis out. He didn't stir. She began to lick his penis and it hardened. This scared her so she left. What was wrong with what she did?

_____

_____

Why might she have done it?

_____

_____

Is it significant that the guy was never awake? _____

Why? _____

_____

6) Johanna's live-in boyfriend never wants to have sex any more, so she buys a bunch of X-rated videos and shows them to him to get him turned on. Is this dysfunctional or healthy? _____

Why? _____

_____

What do you think she is looking for?

_____

_____

What other ways could she choose to get the same thing(s)?

_____

_____

7) If Johanna used the X-rated videos instead to teach her eight-year-old twins about sex, do you think this is healthy or not? _____

Why? _____

_____

What might her real motivations be in doing this?

_____

_____

8) When Marina was taking care of her friend's eleven-year-old son on a hot day, she suggested they go skinny dipping, since she hadn't brought her bathing suit to her friend's house. She took off all her clothes, as did the boy, and they went swimming. Healthy or unhealthy? _____

Why? _____

_____

What if she went skinny dipping with her own family instead? Would it make a difference? _____

Why? _____

_____

9) Carole is a thirty-eight-year-old single mother of a fourteen-year-old son. She is attracted to much younger men. Her current live-in boyfriend is eighteen. Is this healthy or dysfunctional? _____

Why? _____

_____

Why do you think she is attracted to such a young man?

_____

_____

10) Evangelina, who is nineteen, has a boyfriend who is seventeen. Is this likely to be healthy or dysfunctional? _____

_____

_____

Is it significant that her boyfriend is under eighteen? _____

_____

_____

Part 2

Now let's look at you. Have you had healthy sexual experiences? Unhealthy or dysfunctional sexual experiences? This part of the exercise will give you the opportunity to explore your own healthy and dysfunctional sexual history.

As we said before, sex offending is illegally misusing sex to meet your own needs for intimacy or power, to express anger, or to relieve tension and boredom, with someone who doesn't understand and can't or doesn't legally consent.

But what about healthy sex? It is healthy for women to feel sexual and enjoy sex, so long as the sex is consensual, responsible, and doesn't hurt themselves or others.

1) Think about a healthy, pleasurable, and fulfilling sexual experience you have had and describe it below.

Who was your partner?

_____

When in the relationship did the experience occur?

_____

How old were you?

_____

Were you married to or in a committed relationship with this person?

_____

Where did it take place?

_____

What made it healthy, pleasurable, and fulfilling?

_____

_____

What else would you like to tell us about it?

_____

_____

2) Now think about a dysfunctional (unhealthy) sexual experience you have had (other than your sex offense(s) or sex offense(s) committed on you). Describe it below.

Who was your partner?

_____

Were you in a relationship with that person?_____ If so, for how long?_____

What kind of relationship was it?

_____

Where did it take place?

_____

In what ways was it dysfunctional or unhealthy?

_____

_____

How did you feel afterward?

_____

Why do you think that is?

_____

_____

Have you ever repeated the experience?_____ If so, why?

_____

_____

Is there anything else you would like to tell us about it?

_____

_____

3) What were the most significant differences between the healthy and dysfunctional sexual experiences?

_____

_____

4) Describe your sexual offense below.

What did you do?

_____

_____

_____

Was the offense committed by you alone or was another person involved?

_____

If there was another person, who suggested it?

_____

_____

If it was your idea, how did you get your co-offender to go along with it?

_____

_____

If it was the other person's idea, how did that person get you to go along with it?

_____

_____

_____

Was what you did healthy or dysfunctional?_____

Why? _____

What did the victim do?

_____

_____

Do you think the victim liked what was being done? _____

Why or why not? _____

_____

How do you think the victim felt afterward?

_____

_____

How did you feel afterward?

_____

_____

Many people have difficulty saying "Don't do that," or objecting in any other way to being touched. We would like you to remember a time when you didn't want to be touched or didn't like the way you were being touched, but you didn't object. It can be sexual or non-sexual. All of us have been touched at one time or another in ways we didn't like, and some of those times we kept silent about it for one reason or another. For example, Soraya's grandfather would tug at her ear affectionately. It was uncomfortable for her, but she didn't want to tell him because she didn't want to hurt his feelings.

The final exercise for this chapter is a way for you to explore your reactions to the undesirable touches you've experienced, so you can better understand the silence of your victims. As your group members discuss their responses to the touches they describe in this exercise, you will possibly gain additional insight about your sexual-abuse victim's response.

Exercise 19. Touching Assertiveness

1) Think of a time you were touched and didn't like it, but never told the person who touched you how you felt. Who did it and what did that person do?

_____

_____

_____

2) Why didn't you like it?

_____

_____

_____

3) Why didn't you say anything?

_____

_____

_____

4) What could you have said to the person who did it?

_____

_____

_____

5) What effect might that have had on the person who touched you?

_____

_____

_____

6) What effect might that have had on you?

_____

_____

_____

7) If it would not have had a positive effect, what does that tell you about yourself?

_____

_____

_____

8) Can you think of a time, other than your offense, when you touched someone else in a way that the person might not have liked? Describe it.

_____

_____

_____

9) If the person didn't tell you he/she didn't like it, can you understand why the person might not have spoken up? _____ Explain.

_____

_____

_____

10) If the victim of your sex offense never told you to stop, why do you think the victim didn't?

_____

_____

_____

Summary

What you have covered in this chapter:

1) That sex, love, and intimacy are different things.

2) The importance of responsible sex.

3) Different ways sex is misused.

4) How you may have misused sex in your offense.

5) More facts about women and sexuality.

6) Appropriate and inappropriate touching.

7) Why people sometimes don't speak up about uncomfortable touching.

Choices Part II:

Making New Choices for an Offense-Free Life

Chapter 8

Changing Choices, Changing Consequences

We have looked at your sexual offending behavior in several ways: by looking at your personal history—including victimization—choices you've made and their consequences, roles and boundaries, sex and consent, definitions of sexual offending, links in your offense chain, and how your chain becomes a cycle. We will be revisiting some of the same issues, this time looking for how you can change your thoughts, feelings, and choices to prevent yourself from ever reoffending.

Remember your earlier work on positive and negative consequences? All decisions have consequences or results. Most decisions have both positive and negative consequences, pros and cons. Now let's look at a couple of situations of choices and consequences related to sexual offending.

Betty is a sex offender who is really attracted to Bobby. Bobby is cute, fun, pays a lot of attention to her, and has a good job. But he is also an alcoholic and a registered sex offender. Bobby invites Betty to move in with him. If she says no, the main positive consequences are that she will avoid violating her probation or parole and she will be less likely to reoffend, particularly if she doesn't get involved with Bobby at all. The negative consequences are that she will still be alone, she will be giving up a nice place to live, and she will lose a potentially satisfying relationship.

Again, if she says yes, the positive consequences are that she will feel less lonely, she will have a nice place to live, and she will have someone important in her life. The negative consequences are that she might get busted for violating her probation or parole, she might return to alcohol use herself (which was one of the reasons she gave in and helped her last partner commit a sex offense), and she will be placing herself in a position where she is much more likely to be involved in a future sexual reoffense.

Josie also lives by herself and is very lonely. She has noticed one of the boys at her church. She thinks James, who is thirteen, is very mature for his age. He is an orphan who lives in a foster home. She sees he needs love and affection. She would like him to be happier and thinks that if she gives him time and attention outside of the church, she will be helping him. If she decides to invite him to her home for dinner, the positive consequences are that he will feel loved and cared for and she will be less lonely. The negative consequences are that she is placing herself in a position where she might be tempted to have sex with him, may violate her probation or parole conditions not to be alone with a child, may lose her job and self-respect, and could go to prison.

On the other hand, if she chooses not to invite him home, the positive consequences are that she won't violate any conditions of parole or probation, she won't be tempted to get sexually involved with him, she'll keep her self-respect, and she will not be locked up again. The negative consequences are that she will not relieve her loneliness by helping James, and he will have to get attention and affection elsewhere.

Have you ever made lists of pros and cons, or positive and negative results, for decisions you have had to make in the past? Usually people just make two lists—one for the positive consequences or aspects, the other for the negative. In the following exercise, we will be doing that in a detailed way, a way that can help you see both the positive and negative consequences of your choices more clearly.

Before you do the exercise, look at the example that has been filled in below. Abby, an unmarried twenty-one-year-old, is trying to decide whether or not to ask Armando, a twenty-three-year-old she barely knows but would like to know better, to go to a company picnic with her. Her choices are to ask him or not to ask him.

Choice	Positive Consequences	Negative Consequences
If I ask Armando:	1) He might say yes.	1) I can't be turned down.
	2) I'd feel great if he said yes.	2) If I wait and get to know him better, he might come to accept me.
	3) I'd be no worse off than if I if I hadn't asked.	3) There's no chance that we'll have a terrible time.
	4) I'd find out if he likes me.	4) I could still daydream about him liking me without ever having to test reality.
	5) Even if he says no, he might give me some signal that he would go out with me another time.	
If I don't ask Armando:	1) He might turn me down.	1) I'd miss out on a possible great date—maybe he would have gone out with me.
	2) I'd feel embarrassed and/or rotten if he turned me down.	2) He might find someone else in the meantime.
	3) I'd be afraid no man would like me.	3) I might never know if he likes me.
		4) I'd feel like a chicken.

This chart gives Abby a clear way to select her options. It is easier to balance the pros and cons when you can see the good and bad consequences of both doing the act and not doing it.

Most situations involve many more choices than just doing or not doing something. You can use the same chart for all your different options. For example, in her list of choices, Abby might have included asking Armando to help her with a project at work vs. asking him to go to the company picnic, or asking Armando to go to the picnic vs. asking another guy who she knew liked her and probably would accept.

In the next exercise, try out the positive and negative consequences of a past decision you made.

Exercise 20. Positive and Negative Consequences

Part I

In this part of the exercise, think of a time you had to make a decision (not relating to your offense). What were your two major choices? Write them in the Choice column of the chart. Then write down the positive and negative consequences of each.

Choice	Positive Consequences	Negative Consequences
To do:	1)_____	1)_____
	2)_____	2)_____
	3)_____	3)_____
	4)_____	4)_____
	5)_____	5)_____
Not to do:	1)_____	1)_____
	2)_____	2)_____
	3)_____	3)_____
	4)_____	4)_____
	5)_____	5)_____

Filling out this decision chart can help you understand your decision more clearly. Did you make the right one?

Part 2

This time make the same analysis in regard to choices you made that resulted in a sex offense. Look at the positive and negative consequences of that choice. Perhaps if you had weighed all the consequences before committing the offense, you might have acted differently.

Choice	Positive Consequences	Negative Consequences
Commit or participate	1)_____	1)_____
in sex offense	2)_____	2)_____
(your offense)	3)_____	3)_____
	4)_____	4)_____
	5)_____	5)_____
Do not commit or	1)_____	1)_____
participate in sex offense:	2)_____	2)_____
	3)_____	3)_____
	4)_____	4)_____
	5)_____	5)_____

The next time you do your offense chain, do this exercise at each step. You can make your chart more detailed by dividing the consequences into short-term and long-term categories. The chart on the next page does just that. You will usually find that there tend to be positive short-term consequences for things you shouldn't do (immediate gratifications), but the long-term consequences are generally negative and more severe. On the other hand, for decisions you know are right—you may give up some positive consequences/immediate gratifications, but in the long run the consequences will be much more positive.

Try this with some of the choices you have made in your life.

You can use this system with thoughts and feelings as well as behavior. In the next exercise, you will have the opportunity to try this.

Short-Term Consequences

Positive   **Negative**

Choice #1

Positive
1) _____
2) _____
3) _____
4) _____
5) _____

Negative
1) _____
2) _____
3) _____
4) _____
5) _____

Choice #2

Positive
1) _____
2) _____
3) _____
4) _____
5) _____

Negative
1) _____
2) _____
3) _____
4) _____
5) _____

Long-Term Consequences

Positive   **Negative**

Positive
1) _____
2) _____
3) _____
4) _____
5) _____

Negative
1) _____
2) _____
3) _____
4) _____
5) _____

Positive
1) _____
2) _____
3) _____
4) _____
5) _____

Negative
1) _____
2) _____
3) _____
4) _____
5) _____

Remember that you have the power to choose how you *think* about something, what you tell yourself about what's happening and how you're feeling. Changing your self-talk is one way to intervene in your offense cycle so you will feel better about yourself and be less likely to reoffend. There are always many ways of viewing things. Everyone sees things differently. You can look at situations from a different perspective, reframe them for yourself, think about them in a different way.

For example, Peggy's parents never spent any time with her when she was a child, and her grandmother, who raised her, always told her she was no good. A person who goes through this type of situation as a child usually thinks she is worthless and unlovable. As an adult, however, that person can choose to interpret the situation differently. Instead of believing that she is worthless and unlovable, Peggy could work on changing her self-talk, reminding herself that her parents were too young and irresponsible to have children, and her grandmother was a poor substitute who did not know how to raise her. In fact, her grandmother's poor parenting abilities were probably the cause of her mother's inability to appreciate Peggy.

Part 1

Now it's your turn. Pick a time when you felt put down by someone near or dear to you. It could be a parent, other family member, teacher, or friend. What was that situation? Write it here.

_____

_____

_____

_____

_____

_____

You have a choice as to how you think about that put-down. Look at what you wrote. How could you have thought differently about the situation that might have made you feel better about yourself? It could be that the statement said more about the other person than you. For instance, you could have said something to yourself like, "He's upset about something else and is just dumping his problems on me." Or, "She's jealous of the fact that I am smarter or prettier or more talented." Or, "They are mistaken."

Think about it and write down what you could have said to yourself in the above situation that might have made you feel better about the put-down.

_____

_____

_____

_____

_____

_____

_____

Part 2

How you think about that put-down or anything else that is said or done will make a lot of difference not only in how you feel but in what you do as a result. An example is Anna, whose husband told her that she was ugly, fat, and undesirable after she caught him having an affair with another woman. If she tells herself that what he says is true (negative self-talk), she will probably feel very helpless, hopeless, and depressed, and might, as a result, eat or drink too much, fail to take care of her appearance or her home, yell at her children, and so on. On the other hand, if she tells herself that he is just making excuses for his bad behavior, trying to blame her rather than himself, and that she knows she is still attractive and desirable (positive self-talk), she may kick him out and find someone better, insist they go for counseling (if she wants to continue the relationship), and/or find friends who appreciate her.

Think about either the put-down you described or another one and the negative statements (negative self-talk) you might have made to yourself at the time. Then think of the positive statements (positive self-talk) you could have said to yourself instead. How would you behave differently if you thought the put-down was true or if you thought it was not? What difference would it make to how you acted?

Write both the positive and negative self-talk statements below. Put a check beside the one you said to yourself at the time of the put-down. What were the consequences? If you had made the opposite self-talk statement, what would the consequences have been? Note that the consequences can be both feelings and behaviors.

Statements	Feelings	Behaviors
Negative Self-Talk	1)_____	1)_____
Statement	2)_____	2)_____
	3)_____	3)_____
	4)_____	4)_____

Positive Self-Talk	1)_____	1)_____
Statement	2)_____	2)_____
	3)_____	3)_____
	4)_____	4)_____

Can you see how your thoughts about a situation (positive and negative self-talk) have affected both your feelings and your behaviors in all different aspects of your life? And as an adult, you and you alone are responsible for how you choose to interpret situations, and what you do as a result of those interpretations.

In the next exercise, you have the opportunity to look at some poor choices some women offenders made.

Exercise 22. Changing Problem Choices

Read the following scenarios. Then write down all the bad choices that Sandra and Elizabeth made, starting from the beginning. Think about why these decisions were bad. Then write down what better choices they could have made.

Sandra

Sandra is on probation for molesting a neighbor child with her ex-husband. She has no-contact and mandated-treatment conditions. She now lives alone.

One afternoon, she feels hungry. Since there is nothing in the refrigerator at home, she decides to walk to the store. The shortest way is to cut through the schoolyard, so she walks that way. She comes across a child who is looking for a ball. Sandra sees the ball in the bushes and takes the child to it. The child says she's hungry, so Sandra offers to buy her some food at the store if the child will wait for her. When Sandra gets to the store, a young boy is crying in the back because he can't find his mother. Sandra gives him a piece of gum and the boy stops crying. She tells the boy to come with her and they will find his mother. The mother comes along just then, so Sandra pays for her groceries and leaves the store. On the way out, she stops to talk to a group of teenagers hanging out in front of the store. They ask her if she will get some beer for them. She says yes and goes back in to buy them beer. They invite her to party with them that night. She agrees and writes down the address of the party. She leaves then to take the food she bought to the child she had met at the school.

Sandra made at least ten poor choices here. List them in the first column. Then list the better choices she could have made in the second column.

Poor Choices	Better Choices
1) _____	1) _____
2) _____	2) _____
3) _____	3) _____
4) _____	4) _____
5) _____	5) _____
6) _____	6) _____
7) _____	7) _____
8) _____	8) _____
9) _____	9) _____
10) _____	10) _____

Elizabeth

Elizabeth is on probation for molesting her daughter Courtney. She has a no-contact order for Courtney. She is not supposed to see or talk to the child, who lives with her grandmother (Elizabeth's mother). Elizabeth is all by herself in her apartment and feels very lonesome. She calls her mother's home to talk to her mother during the day even though she knows her mother is usually still at work. Courtney answers the phone. She tells Courtney how sorry she is about what she has done, how she loves and misses her, and how she would like to be able to talk to Courtney in person. Courtney says she will come over. When Courtney gets to Elizabeth's apartment, Elizabeth invites her in. They sit on the sofa and talk for a while. Elizabeth begins to think about how loving and warm it would be to touch her daughter's body. Elizabeth asks if she can hug Courtney because she feels so lonely. Courtney agrees. In the process of hugging, Elizabeth's hand accidentally rubs against her daughter's breast. Courtney doesn't say anything and Elizabeth figures, "Since I've gone this far and she doesn't mind, I may as well touch the rest of her." She acts on these thoughts, committing another sex offense.

In this scenario, Elizabeth made ten poor choices. What are they? Include thoughts and feelings as well as behaviors. What better choices could Elizabeth have made?

Poor Choices	Better Choices
1) _____	1) _____
2) _____	2) _____
3) _____	3) _____
4) _____	4) _____
5) _____	5) _____
6) _____	6) _____
7) _____	7) _____
8) _____	8) _____
9) _____	9) _____
10) _____	10) _____

Can you see how Sandra and Elizabeth may have thought they had everything under control or how they may not have been aware of where their actions were leading? They probably did not intend to make bad choices, but they just weren't paying attention to the choices they were making and the likely consequences. They were acting on their feelings and needs rather than thinking things through.

Since you made a significant mistake relative to your offending behavior, you must now be extremely conscious of every step you take that could put you in a situation that could be interpreted as dangerous or could violate the conditions of your release.

So your first treatment goal is to become more conscious of your choices and decisions. Your arms and legs do not move without your choosing to move them. Sex offenses don't just happen. You chose to make the series of decisions that led to committing your offense.

Even if you allowed another person to control your behavior, you made the decision to let that person do so. As we said at the beginning of this chapter, if you are more conscious of your choices and their consequences, you are more likely to make good choices; choices that won't get you into trouble. So think things through before you act.

Another way to make good choices is to look at some of the reasons why you made the past choices you did. Most people who make poor choices and abuse others do it in order to meet their emotional needs. Because they weren't aware of healthy choices, they chose negative (destructive or abusive) ways. Sandra's choices may have been made because she felt crummy about herself and wanted to be liked and looked up to. Elizabeth's choice to see her daughter and hold her and then touch her sexually was a negative way to deal with her loneliness and need to feel loved. Both of them chose to satisfy their needs in ways that were dangerous for them and for the children with them.

There are negative and positive ways to satisfy all the needs you have, ways that won't put you or a potential victim in danger. For example, if Elizabeth felt lonely, she could have called her mother at work or her counselor or a friend. She could have gone over to a friend's house, run around the block or gone to a movie, written a poem or drawn a picture about her loneliness, or talked herself into feeling better by saying, "This loneliness will pass. I can do something positive for myself right now that will make me feel better."

In the next chapter, we'll look at ways you can learn to problem-solve to find the best solutions.

Summary:

You have gained from this chapter:

1) A reminder that you have choices in almost every one of your thoughts, feelings, or actions.

2) Increased awareness that each choice you make has positive and negative consequences.

3) Knowledge about different ways of weighing the consequences of your choices.

4) An understanding of how your needs underlie the choices you make.

5) The knowledge that your self-talk shapes your feelings and behavior.

6) The understanding that by choosing to change your self-talk, you can change your feelings and behavior to stay offense-free.

Chapter 9

Problem-solving: One Part at a Time

A major skill related to making good choices and preventing yourself from reoffending is problem solving. Every problem has lots of solutions (choices that you must make). Some of these solutions are better than others, based on the consequences that happen afterward. Once again, no solutions are all negative or all positive. There are positive and negative consequences to each. When you have a problem, it is a good idea to brainstorm lots of solutions. Make a long list.

If you have friends who can help, make them part of the process. After you make your list, cross out the impossible or clearly negative solutions. Look carefully at the ones you have left. Which ones seem to be better than others? Will you be able to use any of them? What are the likely consequences of each? Think this over carefully. Finally, pick the best one. The best one is the one with the fewest negative results and the most positive results. Be very honest about all the long-term and short-term consequences for you and for anyone else involved. (You can also use your chart of positive and negative consequences to think through the results.)

In the following exercise, you will have the opportunity to generate a variety of solutions to problems, and then to choose the best one. For example, Maria's daughter is flunking her math class. Maria is a former drug user and is the child's sole support. She can't afford a tutor for her daughter. What can she do to help her daughter?

1) Ask a friend who is good at math for help.

2) Learn the materials and try to tutor her daughter herself.

3) Ask at the school about free tutoring.

4) Borrow the money for a tutor from her ex-boyfriend, who is a drug user.

5) Sell drugs to get the money for a tutor.

6) Get a second job tending bar at the corner cafe.

7) Borrow the money from her mother, who will harass her about it forever.

8) Turn tricks (prostitution or exchange sex for money) for a couple of nights.

9) Do nothing and let her daughter sink or swim.

10) Set up a daily study schedule for her daughter and make her stick to it.

11) Tell her daughter she will give her a special treat if she passes math.

12) Borrow the money from a good friend.

13) Ask her pastor if the church has any funds to help kids with school.

As you can see, there are numerous solutions to this problem, as there are to any problem. Some are certainly better than others, and a few are downright terrible. But they are all solutions. Think about which would you choose and why and discuss them with your group and/or therapist.

Every problem you have has multiple solutions. You have to choose the best one by figuring out the consequences of all the possibilities before you act.

Exercise 23. Problem-Solving

For the following problems, write down at least four possible solutions. Then, after thinking of the likely consequences, place a check beside the solution you think would be best.

1. Donna lost her job, and her landlord has threatened to evict her and her children from the apartment she has lived in for three years. She doesn't have deposit money for another apartment. What can she do?

_____ a) _____

_____

_____ b) _____

_____

_____ c) _____

_____

_____ d) _____

_____

2) Carrie loaned her car to her friend Jan, who promptly totaled it. Jan doesn't have insurance, but Carrie does. However, Carrie's insurance will be canceled if she makes another claim. She needs a car for work, but can't afford to buy another one. She wants to keep Jan as a friend. What should she do?

_____ a) _____

_____

_____ b) _____

_____

_____ c) _____

_____

_____ d) _____

_____

3) Diana's boss is sexually harassing her—making lewd remarks and trying to touch her. She likes her job and needs it to live and support her kids, but she wants the harassment to stop. She knows if she goes to the authorities, her boss will fire her, and she probably won't get such good pay again. What can she do?

_____ a) _____

_____

_____ b) _____

_____

_____ c) _____

_____

_____ d) _____

_____

4) Lola's kids come home crying every day because there is a bully on the street who is picking on them. What can she do to stop the bullying?

_____ a) _____

_____

_____ b) _____

_____

_____ c) _____

_____

_____ d) _____

_____

5) Marta is a lesbian. She likes a woman at work named Arletta, who she thinks might like her back, but she isn't sure if Arletta is gay and attracted to her in the same way. What can she do to find out if Arletta is similarly interested in her?

_____ a) _____

_____

_____ b) _____

_____

_____ c) _____

_____

_____ d) _____

_____

6) Tina lost her driver's license for drinking and driving and now has a limited license that only allows her to drive to and from work. Her best friend's daughter is getting married, and the friend, who doesn't drive, begs Tina to drive her to the wedding. Tina doesn't want to disappoint her friend, but she also doesn't want to break the law. What can she do?

_____ a) _____

_____

_____ b) _____

_____

_____ c) _____

_____

_____ d) _____

_____

7) Marge has been going out with someone she really loves. He is pressuring her to have sex, but because of her religious beliefs, she doesn't want to until they get married. She is afraid she will lose him if she doesn't give in. What can she do?

_____ a) _____

_____

_____ b) _____

_____

_____ c) _____

_____

_____ d) _____

_____

8) Terry's son has begun to smack Terry around when he gets angry. Terry does not feel that she can control the boy without calling the police, but is afraid they will arrest and jail him rather than help him. What might Terry do instead?

_____ a) _____

_____

_____ b) _____

_____

_____ c) _____

_____

_____ d) _____

_____

9) Laurie's partner batters her. Laurie doesn't think this is right, but she is afraid that her partner will direct his anger at her children if she says or does anything. What solutions does she have?

_____ a) _____

_____

_____ b) _____

_____

_____ c) _____

_____

_____ d) _____

_____

10) Sue's husband is hooked on crank (methamphetamines). She loves him and depends on him to support the family, but sees that his drug use is negatively affecting their family. What can she do?

_____ a) _____

_____

_____ b) _____

_____

_____ c) _____

_____

_____ d) _____

_____

11) Rhonda caught a neighbor boy molesting his sister in her yard. Rhonda was convicted of child molestation and she is not allowed to be around children unsupervised, so she is afraid to report the molestation for fear her probation will be violated. What can Rhonda do?

_____ a) _____

_____

_____ b) _____

_____

_____ c) _____

_____

_____ d) _____

_____

12) Lorna and her best buddy Lois work for the same firm. Lois is stealing things from the company. Lorna is terrified Lois will be caught, and Lorna will be named as an accessory since they hang around together and Lois drives her to and from work. Lorna was previously arrested because she didn't stop her husband from molesting their son. What should Lorna do?

_____ a) _____

_____

_____ b) _____

_____

_____ c) _____

_____

_____ d) _____

_____

13) Vivian has just found out that she is pregnant. She wants the baby, but is afraid that Children's Protective Services will take the baby away from her because she once passively sat by while her boyfriend molested her daughter. What can she do?

_____ a) _____

_____

_____ b) _____

_____

_____ c) _____

_____

_____ d) _____

_____

14) Nana is on probation for exposing herself. She is attending sex-offender group therapy. She has slipped and exposed herself again a couple of times. She would like to talk about it in group, but is afraid she will be reported and rearrested and even possibly sent to prison. What can she do?

_____ a) _____

_____

_____ b) _____

_____

_____ c) _____

_____

_____ d) _____

_____

As you can see, often there is no perfect solution in these situations. Sometimes it is necessary to compromise on the best of bad solutions. But there are always choices available and some are better than others. Looking at the probable consequences of each choice and balancing them is a way of finding what is likely to work the best.

Sometimes problems feel so overwhelming that you feel immobilized. In such cases, it is best to divide up the problems into little pieces that are manageable. This is called "partializing." It's what they do in Alcoholics Anonymous and other 12-Step programs when they say "one day at a time" or "one minute at a time." Just take a part of one problem you can manage and do that. Then take another little piece of that or another problem and so on, one at a time.

For example, Jeannie's boyfriend has been battering her and her children. She recognizes that it is unsafe to stay with him, but she has no money, no job or job skills, no transportation, and nowhere to go. She has been living in her boyfriend's apartment and he has been supporting her and the kids. She is frightened and overwhelmed by the thought of leaving and having to fend for herself and her four children. To make her problems manageable, she needs to break up her problems into a list according to priorities, then break down each item on the list into even smaller issues. For example:

1) What can she do to find a safe place for her and her children?

   a) Call the emergency women's services hotline or Children's Protective Services and find out if there is a shelter or other temporary housing for herself and her children.

   b) Call the shelter, churches, or whatever other facility might be available.

c) If there is no housing available, call a relative or friend and see if they can provide temporary housing.

d) If there is still no housing available, arrange with Children's Protective Services for the children to go into foster care until she can provide for them.

2) How can she and the children leave without her boyfriend stopping her?

a) Get a court order permitting her to leave with the children and preventing him from stopping her.

b) Pack necessities and leave when her boyfriend is at work.

c) Call a friend, neighbor, a domestic violence shelter worker or the police to transport her and the children to safety.

3) How can she support herself and her children?

a) Once she is in a safe place, she can apply for welfare.

b) She can then look for a job in the newspaper or at the welfare office.

c) She can apply for jobs or job training.

d) She can put up flyers in the markets and post offices offering her services as a house cleaner.

e) She can pick up tin cans and sell them for some small money.

4) How can she prevent her boyfriend from hurting her and the children if he finds her?

a) She can file a criminal complaint with the police department against him.

b) She can go to the courthouse and fill out papers for a restraining order against him.

c) She can call the police if he gets anywhere near her or the children.

d) She can try to always be around other people as a means of protection.

There are also many other subgroups into which she could classify her problems to make them manageable. Notice that by partializing her problems, she has many choices available to her.

Now it's your turn.

Think of a time when you felt really overwhelmed by one or more problems. What was the problem situation?

_____

_____

_____

_____

_____

_____

_____

_____

_____

Now break the situation down into small, manageable parts and describe what you could do for each part. List as many choices as you can for each.

Problem Part 1: _____

What you can do:

1) _____

_____

_____

2) _____

_____

_____

3) _____

_____

_____

4) _____

_____

_____

Problem Part 2: _____

What you can do:

1) _____
   _____
   _____

2) _____
   _____
   _____

3) _____
   _____
   _____

4) _____
   _____
   _____

Problem Part 3: _____

What you can do:

1) _____
   _____
   _____

2) _____
   _____
   _____

3) _____
   _____
   _____

4) _____
   _____
   _____

Problem Part 4: _____

What you can do:

1) _____
   _____
   _____

2) _____
   _____
   _____

3) _____
   _____
   _____

4) _____
   _____
   _____

Problem Part 5: _____

What you can do:

1) _____
   _____
   _____

2) _____
   _____
   _____

3) _____
   _____
   _____

4) _____
   _____
   _____

(You can use additional paper if you have more parts to your problems.)

Remember, you have lots of choices in every aspect of your life. Any time you choose to think, act, or feel a certain way or choose solutions to problems, there are both positive and negative consequences. If you make yourself aware of the consequences, you have the opportunity to make different, healthier choices. You have the power to find different ways to look at things, different ways to act, and different ways to feel based on what you say to yourself. You have the power of choice. Once you realize this, you will also have an easier time solving your problems.

Summary

What you have gained from this chapter:

1) Recognition of choices in problem solving and ways to make better choices

2) The ability to partialize (divide up your problems into manageable pieces)

Chapter 10

Relapse Prevention: Preventing Reoffense

Your most important goal in your treatment is to learn how to prevent yourself from ever offending again. Even if you are sure you would never reoffend, think of completing this workbook as an extra safeguard, because the techniques you are learning will help you to prevent reoffense. In addition, you can apply them to other areas of your life.

In the last chapter you learned how to 'partialize' or break down problems into smaller, more manageable pieces. Now you will learn how to break down your offending behavior into smaller pieces and look at the steps that led you to committing or participating in a sexual offense.

The first method is called "relapse prevention." *Relapse* simply means to fall back into a former way of life after being out of it for a while. In this case, it means committing another sex offense after not having done so for a period of time. And you know what prevention means: stopping it before it happens. In order to stop it, it is important to know how it starts.

To review some of what you learned in part I: Sexual offending is like a chain reaction. We've called it an *offense chain*. The offense chain below shows how you can go from *Seemingly Unimportant Decisions*—we called them "SUDs"—to an offense. It shows how a simple choice can get the whole thing started. Then your choices or decisions along the way can either keep you free from offense, or lead you down the road to reoffending, hurting another person, a child or an adult.

We can picture this reoffense chain as a huge mud hole. In the bottom center is gooey mud (the offense), which you want to avoid. You get closer and closer to the muddy bottom as you fall deeper and deeper in from the sides (move from step to step, from the SUDs downward to the offense). The further down the hole you go, the harder it is to get yourself out. So it is better not to get into it in the first place.

Now take a good look at the diagram below and read the explanations that follow for each of the steps.

The Reoffense Chain

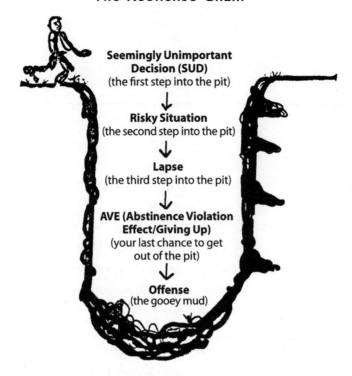

Seemingly Unimportant Decision (SUD)
(the first step into the pit)

↓

Risky Situation
(the second step into the pit)

↓

Lapse
(the third step into the pit)

↓

AVE (Abstinence Violation Effect/Giving Up)
(your last chance to get out of the pit)

↓

Offense
(the gooey mud)

Abstinence (not offending): This means you are not committing any offenses or aiding another person in committing one, and you are planning not to be involved in any offending behaviors. (This does not mean abstaining from healthy sexual behaviors, however. All sex is not bad—only sexual behaviors that hurt others, are against another person's desires, or are done with children are offensive and illegal.)

SUDs (Seemingly Unimportant Decisions): You remember that these are the everyday decisions you make, which seem reasonable, but are risky because they may place you in a potentially offending situation. For example, let's consider Berta. Berta had previously molested her six-year-old daughter. She is home alone watching TV. A neighbor comes to the door and is frantic. Her thirteen-year-old daughter is stranded in a tough part of town, there are no buses at this time of night, and a cab won't come. She asks Berta if she will watch her five-year-old daughter while she goes. Berta agrees. On the surface, saying, "Yes, of course," sounds like a reasonable choice for her to make. But it places Berta in a high-risk situation—on the first rung toward reoffense. It doesn't mean Berta is going to reoffend, but reoffense is more possible.

Risky Situation: This is a dangerous situation because it places you in a position where you have the opportunity to offend. Berta has placed herself in a risky situation by being alone with the child. There is no one to stop Berta if she wants to offend. Again, it doesn't mean Berta is going to reoffend. However, it does put her in a position where it is possible to reoffend.

Lapse: This can be (1) a behavior that brings you very close to a sex offense, or (2) a fantasy or daydream of committing a sex offense.

In our example, perhaps Pearl is crying because her mom isn't there. Berta holds Pearl and slides her hand under the child's pajama top to rub Pearl's back to soothe her. The act of putting her hand on Pearl's back under her pajamas is a lapse. It isn't a sex offense, but it gets very close to one. Berta should not be touching a child's skin under any kind of clothes even for non-sexual reasons. She is only a hair's breadth away from committing a sexual offense. It is much easier to commit an offense when you are in such a risky situation.

Another kind of lapse occurs just in your mind. Perhaps the child is sitting next to Berta on the couch or climbing on her. Pearl reminds Berta of her own daughter, whom she loves dearly. Berta begins to daydream (fantasize) about how it felt to touch her own daughter. She gets an urge to touch the child's private parts. If she doesn't stop the fantasy and urge, this is also called a lapse because it places her that much closer to the forbidden, hurtful sexual act. It makes it much harder to turn away. Lapses are not bad acts in themselves, but they are danger signals you need to do something about.

This second kind of lapse is the kind everyone experiences. You will lapse during or after treatment, no matter how well you've learned relapse prevention skills. Thoughts, memories, fantasies of inappropriate sexual touching with a child or a non-consenting adult almost always come back. It's in learning how to make better choices in dealing with lapses, thoughts, memories, fantasies that will keep you out of trouble and keep those around you safe.

AVE (Abstinence Violation Effect/Giving Up): When you get very close to reoffending, after a lapse like one of the two examples above, it is very easy to slip into the AVE stage. This is where you give up. You figure you have already crossed the line, you have failed, and there is no turning back, so you might as well go ahead and do what you know you really want to do—commit the sexual act. You're at the dangerous, "Oh, what the hell! I may as well do it" point.

Offense: This is molesting a child, raping someone, exposing your genitals, or doing some other illegal sexual activity or abetting (helping) a partner in doing it.

Let's look at what Berta could have done instead of committing the offense—how she could have changed her behavior at each step of the chain.

SUD stage: Berta could have said no to the neighbor: "I'm sorry, I can't watch your child, but I'll make some phone calls to find someone who can." But if she failed to do that and progressed to the risky-situation stage, it still wouldn't be too late. She would still have options to get herself out of the situation.

Risky Situation stage: Berta could have called her roommate, friend, spouse, or another neighbor and asked them to watch the child instead. But if she didn't do that and proceeded to the lapse stage, she still could have avoided reoffending.

Lapse stage: At this point, she could have immediately gotten up and left the room or the apartment, asked someone else to help, or even called her minister to come get the child, if necessary. But if she failed again, she would have one last chance at the Abstinence Violation Effect/Giving Up stage.

AVE (Abstinence Violation Effect/Giving Up) stage: It is still not too late for Berta to stop. Her best bet is to just get out of there, once she has made sure the child is safe. Touching the child's back is not as serious as touching the child's private areas or molesting the child in some other way. If Berta gets out of the house, she will never get to the offense stage.

Exercise 25. Offense Chain

Part 1

Now it is time for you to make your own offense chain in a bit more detail than you have done before. It is often hard to remember exactly what happened and why. If you have problems, just think back to your offense first. Think of what happened, how you felt, and what you did immediately before committing your offense as far back as you can remember. Figuring your offense chain out backwards usually makes it easier. Just write what happened step by step.

Offense (What you did.):

_____

_____

_____

AVE (Abstinence Violation Effect/Giving Up) (At what point did you figure you had already gone too far?):

_____

_____

_____

Lapse (What did you do that was dangerously close to the act and/or when and how did you first fantasize about or get close to doing it?):

Act(s): _____

_____

_____

Fantasies (daydreams about doing the sexual act) or feelings connected to doing the sexual act:

_____

_____

_____

Risky Situation (What was the risky situation or dynamic you were in that preceded the fantasies, feelings, or acts?):

_____

_____

_____

_____

SUD (Seemingly Unimportant Decision) (What happened and what decisions did you make that seemed reasonable at the time, but put you in that position of danger?):

_____

_____

_____

_____

When you finish this exercise, look closely at it. Read each step beginning with the first SUD back through to your offense. Can you see how your very first choice made the offense possible? Did you notice that you could have gotten out of the dangerous situation immediately? And what could you have done when you either started fantasizing, had a feeling, were in a risky situation, or did some act that was very close to offending? Was it really too late to stop after that? Or could you have avoided taking that final step of committing or abetting the sex offense?

These are the questions we will be exploring in a variety of ways as we move along. But first, let's see how you can change that scenario.

Part 2

At each step of the offense chain, fill in what you could have done instead that would have kept you from offending. We will call this the "offense-free" behavior chain because it is the series of behaviors that can help you stay offense-free in the future.

SUD Alternative (What I could have done instead):

_____

_____

_____

Risky Situation Alternative (Where you would have been instead):

_____

_____

_____

Lapse Alternatives (What other thoughts and behaviors you would have had instead):

_____

_____

_____

AVE Giving Up Alternative (What you could have thought or said to yourself instead):

_____

_____

_____

Result: No Offense

Now reread what you wrote. Your alternative behaviors most likely fall into either of two important categories: Avoidance or Escape. If you can avoid getting into a dangerous situation in the first place, you have the best chance of not offending because the opportunity is not present. If you avoid hooking up with a child molester and if you avoid being anywhere near children, you won't take the first step toward molestation. But even if you get into a place of danger, lapse, or are ready to give up, you can still break the chain and not reoffend by escaping from the situation. Leaving is usually the most foolproof way of preventing reoffense.

But there are also other ways. If your offense is child molestation, you can get out of the room the child is in, make sure others are there with you when a child is present, or, if you are trapped in a situation where only you and a child are present, stay in another room or beyond arm's distance from any child.

Staying Out of Trouble: Avoidance & Escape

Avoidance and Escape are the two most important techniques you will ever learn. Engrave them permanently on your brain. Think of them every time you have to make a decision about where to go or what to do. Remember, if you can avoid being in a dangerous place, do so. It is the easiest way to keep from offending. And if you find yourself at risk, escape. Get out of there fast. Get some protection for yourself.

I know you are saying to yourself, "That's silly. I don't have any desire to offend now. Why should I have to change my behavior by always having to avoid and escape?" Again, think of avoidance and escape as a lifeline. If you are not in a situation of danger or if you leave a dangerous situation immediately, you are less likely to slip. Protect yourself by using these two simple words to think ahead and keep yourself safe: avoid and escape.

Exercise 26. Avoidance & Escape

This is an exercise to help you remember Avoidance and Escape. First, take the word "avoidance" and think of as many words or phrases as you can that have the same meaning. Then take the word "escape" and do the same. For example, another phrase for avoidance may be "staying away from," and another word for escape is "getting away." Ask your friends and family for help.

Avoidance can also be thought of as:	Escape can also be thought of as:
1) _____	1) _____
2) _____	2) _____
3) _____	3) _____
4) _____	4) _____
5) _____	5) _____
6) _____	6) _____
7) _____	7) _____
8) _____	8) _____

9) _____   9) _____

10) _____   10) _____

If you can't think of any other words or phrases that mean the same as avoidance and escape, go to your dictionary. Look up these words. The dictionary will give you some words and phrases you can use to complete this exercise and might help you better understand what these words mean.

Remember to use Avoidance and Escape properly, however. Use them only to keep yourself from getting into dangerous situations or trouble. Avoiding talking about your offense, avoiding therapy, avoiding feelings, or avoiding people in general will only help you get into more trouble in the future. Likewise, if you escape from your responsibilities or from dealing with your problems, you will only make things more difficult for yourself in the long run. Don't apply these concepts or any others blindly. Use reason and common sense.

Just to make sure you understand when and when not to avoid or escape, complete the following short exercise.

Exercise 27. Using Avoidance & Escape Properly

Write "yes" in front of each example where Avoidance or Escape is used properly and "no" before each example where it is misused.

1) _____ Mary Ellen taught school until she molested a seven-year-old girl in her class. She is now working in a grocery store. A young girl tells her she needs to use the bathroom and asks Mary Ellen to take her to it. Mary Ellen avoids being alone with the child by asking another clerk to show her to the bathroom.

2) _____ When Doreen worked as a preschool teacher, she molested one of the little boys in her class. On the way back from her new job one afternoon, she cut through a deserted park and decided to swing on one of the swings. A little boy she knew came up and sat in the swing next to her and asked to be pushed. Doreen said no and left, escaping the situation.

3) _____ Alicia was frustrated when a male coworker got the promotion she wanted. She found herself thinking about making obscene phone calls to the coworker. When asked in sex-offender group how she was doing, she said she was fine and avoided thinking or talking about her telephone fantasies.

4) _____ Roberta has a history of exposing herself. Roberta's husband yelled at her because the house was a mess and the children were cranky. Roberta went for a drive to escape from her husband's anger.

5) _____ Carla was with her boyfriend and another woman. The two of them wanted to have sex with a teenage boy they knew was bisexual. They talked about taking him into their garage and paying him to have sex with all of them. Carla said, "count me out" and left, escaping from the situation.

6) _____ Toni had previously molested a young boy. Her sister was babysitting a young child. Her sister had an emergency and had to go, leaving the child with Toni. Toni immediately called a friend to watch the child and then walked out, escaping the situation.

7) _____ Belia found herself peeking into the men's dressing room at her gym. She was very embarrassed about her behavior, but since she hadn't been caught she didn't tell anyone, thus avoiding further embarrassment or consequences.

8) _____ Maria was very unhappy. The last time she was unhappy, she had molested her daughter. Maria decided to go to her own room, where nobody would see her unhappiness and bother her about it. (Was this avoidance or escape? Circle one.)

9) _____ Karen refused to talk about her offense in group, saying she had put it behind her. (Was this avoidance or escape? Circle one.)

10) _____ Elena was at a party. Everyone was getting drunk. The host's children were sleeping in the bedroom. As Elena was picking up her coat from the bed there, she accidentally brushed a young boy's thigh with her arm. It excited her. She ran out of the room. (Was this avoidance or escape? Circle one.)

If you are not sure about the answers to any of these questions, talk to your counselor or the other members in group. These questions should help you remember when Avoidance and Escape are properly and improperly used.

Exercise 28. Using Alternative Thoughts & Behaviors

Part I

Complete the following scenarios by writing in an appropriate escape or avoidance behavior that could break the offense chain and prevent reoffense.

1) Juanita previously molested her teenage son. One afternoon, when she is alone in the garage looking through the storage, a neighbor boy comes into the garage and starts to talk to her. Juanita should:

_____

_____

_____

2) Martha's ex-husband made her help him molest a preteen girl in the neighborhood. Martha's new boyfriend has a daughter who is about the same age as the victim. He tells Martha that he has been fantasizing about molesting his daughter. Martha should:

_____

_____

_____

3) Jane is babysitting for a friend. She is changing the baby's diaper, when she has the urge to play with the little boy's penis. She should:

_____

_____

_____

4) Rosa molested a girl and boy she used to babysit. She misses the children because they really loved her. The little girl calls her up on the telephone. Rosa should:

_____

_____

_____

5) In scenario 4, Rosa doesn't want to reject the child because the child is motherless and needy. What could she do to help the child?

_____

_____

_____

6) Phyllis has previously exposed herself to young children in her former neighborhood. She is working as a delivery person for a florist. She notices that the most direct route to her next delivery is right past the street where she exposed herself. It is 4:00 PM, and she is late. She should:

_____

_____

_____

7) Dora has previously molested two little boys. She is over at her divorced friend Tanya's house watching a special on TV. Tanya runs out of cigarettes and decides to go to the store for more. Tanya's young son lives with her and is due home from school at any minute. Dora should:

_____

_____

_____

8) In the same scenario, Dora decides to stay and finish watching the special. Tanya's son comes home and joins Dora in the TV room. Dora should:

_____

_____

_____

9) Next, Tanya's son asks Dora to help him with his homework. Dora sits on the sofa next to him and starts to help him. She begins to fantasize about touching the boy's private parts. Dora should:

_____

_____

_____

10) Then, Dora places her hand on the boy's leg. She begins to feel like a failure because she has forgotten all the relapse-prevention lessons she learned in her treatment group. She figures Tanya's son will tell that she put her hand on the his leg, so, what the hell, why not touch his penis? At this point, Dora should:

_____

_____

_____

11) Janet is over at her friend's house. Her friend's teenage son says, "Hey, Janet, I've got an awfully stiff neck. Would you rub it for me?" Janet begins to massage the boy's neck and feels herself getting aroused. Janet should:

_____

_____

_____

Think of some situations in your own life where, if you don't use the appropriate avoidance and escape actions, you could be in a risky situation, lapse, give up, or reoffend. What avoidance and escape actions could you take at each step? Discuss this with your group or your therapist.

Part 2

Looking at things from a different perspective at each step can also help you change your behavior—what you subsequently do. As we learned before, it is easier to change your behavior when you look at things from a different angle, changing your thinking or self-talk. For this part of the exercise, review each of the scenarios above and write down what you could say to yourself to help you appropriately avoid or escape similar dangerous situations.

1) _____

_____

_____

2) _____

_____

_____

3) _____

_____

_____

4) _____

_____

_____

5) _____

_____

_____

6) _____

_____

_____

7) _____

_____

_____

8) _____

_____

_____

9) _____

_____

_____

10) _____

_____

_____

11) _____

_____

_____

Can you see how the way you think can affect your behavior?

Summary:

In this chapter on preventing reoffense, you had the opportunity to learn:

1) What relapse prevention means.

2) The steps in an offense chain—SUD (Seemingly Unimportant Decision), Risky Situation, Lapse, AVE (Abstinence Violation Effect/Giving Up), Offense.

3) The steps in your own behavioral chain.

4) Alternative actions you can take to prevent offending.

5) The importance and use of Avoidance and Escape to prevent reoffense or accusations.

Chapter 11

Triggers and Risk Factors

Triggers are problematic or painful situations that cause you to feel painful emotions. These painful emotions, which could lead toward dysfunctional or deviant behaviors such as sex offending, are called risk factors. The first step is to be aware of your triggers and what you feel when they occur. Then you will be able to lessen the impact of the risk factors by doing positive things that will make you feel better without harming anyone.

For example, Johanna's mother is always putting her down, telling her how fat and unattractive she is. This triggers her belief that no man will ever want her, and in turn she feels unlovable, worthless, unattractive, and undesirable—all risk factors for her. These risk factors could lead to her turning to one of her junior-high students for a sexual relationship because she believes nobody her own age will want her. But she doesn't have to go in that direction. Instead, she can decrease her risk factors by going out with friends who like her, helping at an old people's home where she is always appreciated, enrolling in Weight Watchers and starting to lose weight, working out at the gym, or going to a single's affair where she might meet someone who is attracted to her. If she does any or all of these things, she will have successfully coped with her risk factors and won't feel the need to find a youngster to satisfy her needs.

An extreme example is that of Jenny. Jenny's boyfriend Jerry tells her she is a loser and lousy in bed, and that he needs more sexual variety. He threatens to leave her if she doesn't help him find a teenage girl to have sex with. This is a trigger for Jenny because it makes her feel inadequate, frightened of losing him, and depressed, which are clearly risk factors for her. She wants to keep Jerry because she is afraid of being alone. But does she have to offend in order to do so? Does she really need such a person in her life? She has the power to diffuse her feelings of inadequacy, fearfulness, and depression in a variety of ways. She can go to church and talk to her pastors. She can go to Parents Without Partners and meet other men who will be attracted to her. She can talk to her therapist. She can visit a friend who will bolster her ego. She can call Jerry's probation officer to let him know Jerry is slipping. She can go out and play a round of golf, which is her favorite sport and which she plays well. She can do any number of other things. Can you think of any others?

Exercise 29. Defusing My Triggers

Part 1

Now it's your turn. Think of a situation that triggers your risk factors. Write it down in the chart below. Then recognize and write down three of the risk factors that arise from that trigger. Finally, write down at least three ways you can defuse (lessen the power of) those risk factors. Do this exercise with at least two different triggering situations.

Triggers	Risk Factors	Ways of Diffusing Risk Factors
First Situation	1)_____	1)_____
	2)_____	2)_____
	3)_____	3)_____
Second Situation	1)_____	1)_____
	2)_____	2)_____
	3)_____	3)_____
Third Situation	1)_____	1)_____
	2)_____	2)_____
	3)_____	3)_____

Part 2

Now take a 3 x 5 card and write down your risk factors on the front side and all the ways you can defuse or minimize them on the back side. Carry this card around with you at all times. When you are feeling bad, take it out, read both sides, and do some of the things you wrote down to defuse or minimize the effect of the risk factors.

Part of what we are looking at in these exercises is how thoughts and feelings can affect how you act or behave. For example, if someone pushes you as you are walking down the street, and you think they are doing it deliberately, you are likely to get angry and either say something nasty or push them back. But if you think they have accidentally tripped and fallen against you, you instead will probably look to see if they are hurt and then offer help. You won't feel angry, so you won't yell or push back.

This same idea applies to the offense chain and offense cycle. How you think and feel can determine if you will offend again or act in some other inappropriate way. This is why it is important to be able to interpret a situation in different ways (change your thoughts) depending on what is actually happening, to see how your different thoughts about the situation affect your emotions, and to look at what your probable actions might be depending on how you are feeling.

In the pushing example above, you can see how your thinking might be in error. You might have distorted what occurred based on experiences you've had in the past. But the same reasoning might not apply now. The situation might be totally different. We call these erroneous or distorted thoughts "thinking errors." Once again, if you think about something wrongly by interpreting a situation inaccurately, you can affect your feelings, which will affect your actions.

The following short exercise can help you see that there may be different ways of thinking about the same situation.

Exercise 30. Changing Thoughts

For each of the following scenarios, write down what you think has happened. Then change your thinking to come up with another possible way you could look at the situation. For example, you see a man holding a woman firmly by the arm, hurrying her down the street. Your first thought is that she's being kidnapped. But other possibilities include that they are late for an appointment or rushing to the hospital to see a family member. Now it is your turn.

1) You co-workers look at you and whisper to each other as you come in.

Your first thought:

_____

_____

What it could be instead:

_____

_____

2) Your daughter hides her school papers and won't show them to you.

Your first thought:

_____

_____

What it could be instead:

_____

_____

3) You come home from work and see your husband packing his suitcase.

Your first thought:

_____

_____

What it could be instead:

_____

_____

4) Your neighbor hates your young cat. You come home from work and find the cat dead.

Your first thought:

_____

_____

What it could be instead:

_____

_____

5) You go to your friend's wedding. There are several nice-looking men there, but none of them talk to you or ask you to dance.

Your first thought:

_____

_____

What it could be instead:

_____

_____

6) Your girlfriend leaves you for another woman.

Your first thought:

_____

_____

What it could be instead:

_____

_____

7) Your mother neglected you when you were a child, forgetting to feed you, spending her money on her own clothes rather than yours, and spending all her time with her boyfriends.

Your first thought:

_____

_____

What it could be instead:

_____

_____

8) Your father always called you names like "stupid slut" and "dumb whore" when you were growing up.

Your first thought:

_____

_____

What it could be instead:

_____

_____

9) Your co-worker just got the promotion you wanted and thought you deserved.

Your first thought:

_____

_____

What it could be instead:

_____

_____

10) Your boyfriend won't invite you to any of his family gatherings.

Your first thought:

_____

_____

What it could be instead:

_____

_____

You can see how differently you would feel and perhaps act if you changed the way you think about a situation. In the next exercise, you have the opportunity to apply what you have learned to offending and avoiding reoffense.

Exercise 31. Putting Thoughts, Feelings & Behaviors into the Offense Chain and Cycle

Another way to break down your offense chain and cycle into manageable pieces is by looking at your thoughts, feelings, and emotions at each step. How could you have changed your self-talk (what you think or say to yourself)? What could you have done to feel better? What strategies could you have used to prevent reoffense at each step? Fill in the blanks first with what you thought, felt, and did before offending, and then with what you could have done (offense-prevention strategies).

1) What do you think triggered your offense?

_____

_____

_____

2) What thoughts, feelings, and behaviors followed? Record them in the spaces on the next page.

Thoughts lead to	**Feelings** which lead to	**Behaviors**
Negative thoughts	Painful feelings (risk factors)	What did you do?
_____	_____	_____
_____	_____	Risky situation_____
_____	_____	_____
_____	_____	_____
Thoughts or fantasy of offense (lapse)	Feelings when thinking of offense	Further risky situation(s)
_____	_____	_____
_____		_____
_____	Feelings just before offense _____	Lapse actions _____
_____	_____	_____
_____	_____	_____
AVE (Giving up thoughts)	Feelings at time of offense	Offense actions
_____	_____	_____
_____	_____	_____
_____	_____	_____
_____	_____	_____
Thoughts right after offense	Feelings right after offense	Actions right after the offense
_____	_____	_____
_____	_____	_____
_____	_____	_____
Later	Later	Later
_____	_____	_____
_____	_____	_____
_____	_____	_____

3) Now think of what you could have done at each of these points to avoid offending. How could you have changed your self-talk? What could you have done to feel better? What avoidance and escape strategies could you have used to prevent reoffense at each step? Fill in the blanks with offense-prevention strategies, recognizing that how you think about things affects how you feel, which in turn affects how you behave.

Thoughts lead to	Feelings which lead to	Behaviors
Change thoughts to:	Things to do about painful feelings:	Different actions at SUD stage
_____	_____	_____
_____	_____	_____
_____	_____	_____
_____	_____	In a risky situation _____
_____	_____	_____
Change thoughts or fantasy of offense (lapse) to:	Things to do if you still have painful feelings	Different actions if still in a risky situation, but feeling better
_____	_____	_____
_____	_____	_____
_____	_____	After a lapse act _____
_____	_____	_____
Change AVE (Giving-up thoughts) to:	Things to do to change painful giving-up feelings:	Alternative to offense actions:
_____	_____	_____
_____	_____	_____
_____	_____	_____
_____	_____	

To be safe and to keep others safe, it is important to develop careful plans to keep yourself from reoffending. By understanding your behavior chain and offense cycle and the thoughts (self-talk), behaviors, and feelings that got you into trouble, you can make the changes necessary to have a happier life and prevent yourself from reoffending.

You have learned from this chapter on triggers and risk factors

    1) What triggers are

    2) What risk factors are

    3) How you can defuse triggers and risk factors through more positive self-talk

    4) How your thoughts or self-talk and your emotions can change your behavior

    5) What thinking errors are and how to change your thinking

If you feel confused about any of these ideas, read the chapter over, talk to your treatment provider, or talk to your friends in group.

Chapter 12

Identifying Feelings

Many women who have committed or participated in sexual offenses are out of touch with what they are feeling. You might have closed off your emotions because of your own experiences of childhood abuses and traumas. You might be acting out (or acting in) your feelings instead of allowing yourself to experience them. That's a problem because if you cannot feel your own emotions, you certainly cannot feel or connect with what your victims might be experiencing.

You might shut down your awareness of what victims feel when you choose satisfying your own needs over the well-being of your victims. Or if you are aware of your painful feelings, but do not have adequate ways to process them, you are more likely to use thinking errors and distortions and to behave in a way that is self-destructive or dangerous to others.

This part of *Choices* is about helping you learn skills to prevent yourself from reoffending. Identifying your emotions, meeting your emotional needs in a healthy way, and keeping yourself aware of the feelings of others will help.

First, it is important to develop a vocabulary of feelings. Following is a brief list of some of the words we use to describe our emotions:

afraid	cold	dumb
aggravated	content	ecstatic
aloof	courageous	embarrassed
amused	curious	energetic
angry	defiant	excited
anxious	depressed	exhausted
ashamed	detached	fearful
bashful	determined	flippant
bored	dirty	frantic
cautious	disgusted	friendly
cheerful	down	frightened

frustrated	jealous	sad
good	joyful	satisfied
goofy	lonely	selfish
grateful	loving	sexy
guilty	mad	shaky
happy	nervous	shy
hateful	optimistic	silly
helpless	overwhelmed	smothered
hopeful	panicked	sorry
hopeless	paranoid	stupid
hostile	peppy	tearful
humiliated	perplexed	thankful
hungry	pessimistic	threatened
hurt	playful	tough
hyper	pleased	troubled
hysterical	powerful	unhappy
impatient	put-out	unique
inadequate	regretful	uptight
independent	relieved	vengeful
indifferent	resentful	whipped
insecure	responsible	wicked
irritated	ridiculous	worried
isolated	rotten	wounded

Read over these feeling words. Think about what they mean. (If you don't know the meaning of a word, look it up in a dictionary.) Can you think of a time in your life when you felt any of these? Think of other feeling words that aren't on the list.

The following exercises will increase your understanding and use of feeling words.

Exercise 32. Using Feeling Words

Part 1

Write a short story or poem using twelve of the feeling words from the list above. Use extra paper if you need it.

_____

_____

_____

_____

_____

_____

_____

_____

_____

_____

_____

_____

_____

_____

_____

_____

_____

_____

_____

_____

_____

_____

Part 2

On separate sheets of blank paper draw a picture or design that expresses each of these feeling words: sorrow, joy, rage, nervousness, strength, helplessness, betrayal. Don't worry if the pictures don't look like anything in particular. Just imagine the emotions, and using color and texture, let yourself go.

Part 3

Our bodies also express our emotions. When you are sad, you are likely to slump, hang your head down, and move slowly and heavily. When you are furious, your motions may be sharp and quick, you may pound with your fists and stamp your feet, and your voice may go up several notches. You can play emotional charades in your group by giving each member an emotion to act out. The rest of the group must guess which it is. Or you can make up a dance using several emotion words, using your body movements to express each of the feelings.

Another way to incorporate feelings into your vocabulary is to apply them to various situations. The exercise below will help you with that.

Exercise 33. Feelings Sentence Completion

1. Complete the following sentences, describing the situation in which you felt the feeling listed.

a) I felt happy when _____

b) I worried that _____

c) I was most angry when _____

d) I felt loneliest when _____

e) I felt appreciated when _____

f) I felt abandoned when _____

g) I was calmest when _____

h) I was frustrated with _____

i) I felt excited when _____

j) I felt bitter toward _____

2) Now do the same type of exercise the other way around. This time describe the feeling after the situation. Complete the following sentences, using different feeling words for each sentence.

a) When someone is rude to me, I feel _____

b) When someone is kind to me, I feel _____

c) When someone puts me down, I feel _____

d) When I say something dumb, I feel _____

e) When I'm wrongfully accused of something, I feel _____

f) When my partner cheats on me, I feel _____

g) When I can't do something I am trying to do, I feel _____

h) When I get caught doing something wrong, I feel _____

i) When I talk to someone I really like, I feel _____

j) When I'm criticized, I feel _____

k) When my friends ignore me, I feel _____

Another way to increase your awareness of your emotions is to take your "emotional temperature." There is no thermometer for this. You just have to check in with yourself and notice what you are feeling. You may find that you were not aware of some of your emotions.

One way to figure out how you feel is to be aware of your body. If you pay attention, your body will give you clues as to what emotion you are experiencing. For example, if you are angry:

Does your face get red or feel hot?

Do your muscles tense up?

Does your breathing change?

Do you feel sick?

Does your voice get higher or lower? Louder or softer?

Does your head pound?

Do you feel more energetic or powerful?

Does your posture change? How?

You probably experience some of these physical signs of anger, but maybe not all of them at the same time. Be aware of which ones apply to you. Then, for example, if you find your muscles tensing, voice getting higher, and energy pulsing, you can clue yourself in that you are probably feeling angry.

And as we talked about before, when you are depressed, you might slump, cross your arms over your chest to keep people out, speak more softly or mumble, and/or frown. When you are anxious or nervous, your voice may get quivery and you may fidget and tap, move around a lot, feel racy inside, and have difficulty sleeping. Every time your body language changes, notice what emotions you may be feeling, and every time you are aware of your emotions, notice how your body is reacting. Increased awareness of emotions can help you think before you act and make better choices in dealing with painful feelings. For people who tend to impulsively act out their emotions, this is a way of slowing down and taking more well-thought-out actions.

Although depression, anger, frustration, inadequacy, fear, or other painful emotions probably played a part in your sexual offending, there are no "bad" emotions. All feelings are normal and okay. It is what you *do* with the emotions that is important because, as you have read before, your feelings (which are affected by your thoughts) affect your behavior. If you are aware of your emotions and express them appropriately, you are less likely to reoffend.

Exercise 34. Recording Emotions

For three days, record what you are feeling at the times of day listed below. Use the feelings listed in the beginning of the chapter, not just "good," "bad," or "okay."

1) First thing in the morning when you wake up:

Day 1 _____

Day 2 _____

Day 3 _____

2) During lunchtime:

Day 1 _____

Day 2 _____

Day 3 _____

3) Mid-afternoon:

Day 1 _____

Day 2 _____

Day 3 _____

4) At 6:00 PM:

Day 1 _____

Day 2 _____

Day 3 _____

5) Just before you go to bed:

Day 1 _____

Day 2 _____

Day 3 _____

Did you have a hard time with the last exercise? Did you write "okay" or "the same" on any of the lines? If you did, change it to a fitting emotion word from the list at the beginning of this chapter. Our emotions at these different times may not have been very different or extreme, but there may have been other events that triggered more distinct emotions—even just for a minute or two. Don't overlook those little emotional changes.

How have you handled your emotions in the past? In the next exercise, you will look at the various ways you may have expressed several different emotions. Did your parents handle feelings in the same way? How did you feel when they handled their feelings toward you in that way?

Exercise 35. Expressing Emotions

1) **Anger**

a) How many of the following ways have you expressed or handled your anger? Put a check mark next to the ones that apply.

_____ Yelled or screamed

_____ Hit someone

_____ Hit something

_____ Broke something

_____ Cried

_____ Ran away

_____ Just held it in

_____ Wrote out your feelings

_____ Drank or used drugs

_____ Gave the silent treatment

_____ Said something nasty

_____ Took out your feelings on someone other than who you were mad at

_____ Said something to hurt someone back

_____ Did physical exercise (played basketball, went jogging, lifted weights, etc.)

_____ Swore

_____ Said something sarcastic

_____ Did something creative (art, woodwork, or ?)

_____ Thought about having revenge

_____ Took a time out

_____ Talked out your feelings calmly at the time

_____ Talked out your feelings calmly later

_____ Committed a sex offense

_____ Changed your thinking about the situation

_____ Took out your feelings on yourself:

    _____ cut yourself

    _____ attempted suicide

    _____ other _____

_____ Any other ways? _____

_____

b) Which of these ways of expressing anger are most healthy or productive for you? Circle them. Why do you think they are healthy or work best?

_____

_____

Did you feel better after you did them? _____

Was anyone hurt? _____

Did it help solve the situation that triggered your anger? _____

Did you have to pay for damages or treatment for injuries (yours or someone else's)?

_____

c) Look at your most unhealthy responses. Why are they unproductive ways of expressing anger?

_____

_____

d) Since changing your thoughts can affect how you feel about things, what could you say to yourself that might make you feel less angry?

_____

_____

e) What activities could you do that might make you feel less angry?

_____

_____

2) **Depression** (feeling down or blue)

a) Which of the following ways have you used to express or handle your feelings of depression? (Check them below)

____ Cried

____ Read

____ Drank alcohol

____ Hurt yourself

____ Used street drugs or prescription pain killers

____ Ate

____ Slept

____ Got angry

____ Withdrew (stayed alone)

____ Attempted suicide? (How?_____)

____ Wrote out your feelings

____ Did physical exercise

_____ Did something creative

_____ Hit something

_____ Took your feelings out on someone else (including sex offending)

_____ Watched TV

_____ Beat someone up

_____ Went shopping

_____ Had sex

_____ Talked to a friend

_____ Moaned

_____ Other ways

b) Circle the ways you expressed depression in a positive way. Why are these healthy?

_____

_____

c) Now look at your most destructive or unhealthy ways. Why are they harmful?

_____

_____

d) What could you say to yourself to help you feel less depressed?

_____

_____

e) What could you have done that would make you feel less depressed?

_____

_____

3) **Anxiety** (worry, nervousness, etc.)

a) Which of the following ways have you used to express or handle your anxiety? (Check them on the next page)

_____ Dwelled on it (kept worrying)

_____ Paced

_____ Yelled or screamed

_____ Cried

_____ Withdrew (stayed alone)

_____ Ran away

_____ Overate and threw up

_____ Held your feelings in

_____ Wrote out your feelings

_____ Cut on yourself

_____ Did something creative

_____ Punched the wall

_____ Struck someone

_____ Made lists of things to do

_____ Ran or did other physical exercise

_____ Talked about your feelings with someone who would understand

_____ Took out your feelings on yourself by attempting suicide

_____ Masturbated

_____ Other ways

b) Again, circle the most positive or healthy ways of expressing anxiety. Then look at the unhealthy or destructive ways you have handled your anxiety. Can you see why they were not healthy for you? (List why)

_____

_____

_____

c) What positive self-talk might make you feel a little less anxious?

_____

_____

_____

d) What could you do that might relieve some of the anxiety?

_____

_____

_____

You can do the same exercise with any emotions that bother you or cause you problems, such as fear (of abandonment, being alone, etc.), frustration, powerlessness, loneliness, hopelessness, resentment, jealousy, or humiliation. There are lots of painful emotions. Think of some you tend to feel and write them in the space provided.

_____

_____

We talked about triggers in the last chapter. Reread that section if you don't remember what was said. Triggers are so important that we'll do a little more work on understanding them and how they affect our emotions and actions.

Depression may be triggered by many of the same experiences as anger, and it can also be triggered by experiences in which people feel helpless, inadequate, worthless, lonely, or like a failure. Anxiety is often triggered by uncertainty, lack of control, and inability to solve a problem.

You may not be aware of the triggering event. You may not realize what "sets you off." You may think you feel the way you do for some reason that has nothing to do with what really started your painful emotions. At other times, events may build one upon the other, so there may be multiple triggers. For example, maybe your husband was in a terrible mood when he came home from work and yelled at you, you find out your fifteen-year-old daughter is pregnant, and the school called to tell you that your son was expelled for fighting. These may trigger a variety of painful emotions in you.

Think of some of the times you felt angry, depressed, and anxious. What was the trigger? What happened just before you started feeling those emotions? If you can identify and understand your triggers and how you tend to react, you are more likely to be able to make choices about how to respond in ways that keep you safe and out of trouble. You may be able to choose behaviors or say things to yourself (change your self-talk) that will help you feel better more quickly.

Some people have trouble identifying any emotion other than anger. If you are having this difficulty, ask your therapist for help in figuring out what other emotions you may be covering up with your feelings of anger. These emotions might include hurt, rejection, betrayal, sadness, loneliness, among other painful feelings.

When you do the following exercise, check to see whether anger is the only painful emotion you can list. Anger is often a mask for feelings of hurt and betrayal—it's easier to feel angry than hurt. If that happens, take extra time to look beneath the anger to the feeling that was triggered by the event. Remember, your therapist and/or members of your treatment group can help.

This exercise will help you understand the tie-in between your emotions, your triggers, what you say to yourself (self-talk), and the outcomes or results in a slightly different way than we did before. Remember, you can either make yourself feel better or worse, depending on how you think about what has happened.

Exercise 36. Changing Emotions & Outcomes

Part 1

First, think of three times you felt really rotten—frustrated, angry, depressed, or whatever—and there were negative outcomes or results from the experiences. Write down the emotion you felt at the time, identify the triggering event (what happened to bring it on), what you thought and said to yourself at the time, and what the negative result was.

Emotion	Triggering Event	Negative Self-Talk	Result
1)_____	_____	_____	_____
2)_____	_____	_____	_____
3)_____	_____	_____	_____

Part 2

For the next part of this exercise, think of three times you felt good—happy, excited, relaxed, or whatever—and there were positive outcomes from the experiences. Write down the emotion you felt at the time, what caused you to feel good (triggering event), what you were thinking at the time, and what was the positive result was.

Emotion	Triggering Event	Positive Self-Talk	Result
1)_____	_____	_____	_____
2)_____	_____	_____	_____
3)_____	_____	_____	_____

Part 3

For the final part of this exercise, go back to part 1. Write down the emotions and triggering events just as you did before, but change your negative self-talk to more positive statements that might help you get out of your painful feelings. Then write what the changed result might turn out to be.

Emotion	Triggering Event	Positive Self-Talk	Possible Result
1)_____	_____	_____	_____
2)_____	_____	_____	_____
3)_____	_____	_____	_____

This exercise can help you understand how you can choose either to make your feelings worse, and thus make the outcome or results worse, or to make yourself feel a little better, with better results, depending on how you think and talk to yourself about what is happening. Try it in real life and see how it works. It isn't foolproof, but if you practice changing your thoughts and feelings into more positive ones, you are likely to have a better time in life. Things may go more smoothly for you, and you will be less likely to act out your emotions in destructive ways. What you are learning here is something you need to apply forever.

The following Thinking Through Emotions exercise ties together your feelings, what is happening, how you experience your emotion(s) physically, what you say to yourself, and what happens. Keep a copy of this sheet with you in your pocket or wallet, and some time when everything seems to turn out terribly, take it out and fill in the blanks. Answer the questions, then correct your thinking, see what effect it has on your emotions, and how it might change the results. This might help you see all the connections and understand the real power you have over yourself, your feelings, your actions, and your life in general.

Exercise 37. Thinking Through Emotions

Emotion (What emotions am I feeling?)

_____

_____

Situation and Setting (Where am I? Who am I with? What is happening, or what am I doing?)

_____

_____

_____

_____

Symptoms (How am I experiencing the emotion physically?)

_____

_____

_____

Thoughts (What am I thinking about what is going on?)

_____

_____

_____

Results (Behavior: What do I do or not do as a result?)

_____

_____

_____

Corrected Thoughts (What other ways can I think about what is going on?)

_____

_____

_____

Effect on Emotions (What effect do my changed ways of thinking have on my feelings?)

_____

_____

_____

Changed Results (How could my changed thoughts and feelings affect what I do or don't do in this situation?)

_____

_____

_____

In the next chapter we will put your newly identified feelings to good use in learning about empathy.

Summary:

In this chapter on emotions, you had the opportunity to:

1) Learn more words to describe your emotions.

2) Increase your awareness of what you are feeling at any given time and in any situation.

3) Increase your awareness of how certain feelings are expressed in your body.

4) Find positive ways of handling and expressing emotions.

5) Gain knowledge of how you can change your emotions through more positive self-talk.

6) Have a better understanding of how both emotions and thoughts affect behavior.

7) Understand how thoughts, feelings, and behavior interact in the offense chain and what to do for a more positive outcome.

Chapter 13

Empathy: Understanding Others' Feelings

Empathy is one of the most important qualities you can develop. It is the one most often forgotten by sex offenders when they commit or participate in a sex offense. Empathy means trying to understand what another person is likely to be thinking and feeling in a given situation. It means trying to put yourself in their shoes.

No two people react to things in the same way. For example, Alberta, an eleven-year-old girl, felt confused and embarrassed when her aunt molested her, while Alice, another eleven-year-old who was also molested by an aunt, felt helpless, invaded, and terrified. Both had painful feelings, but their feelings were different. The way the molestations happened, the personalities and prior experiences of each of the girls, the relationship each had with her own aunt, and many other factors affected their individual responses.

Another example: Two thirteen-year-old boys received a series of obscene phone calls from an unknown woman. Bill was disgusted and frightened; disgusted because the things that were said were crude, and frightened because he didn't know if that person was working alone or with a man or if one or both might come to his home and hurt him. He felt sick to his stomach and had nightmares about the calls. Bob, on the other hand, just thought the calls were a joke.

Another situation is that of Tony and Chuck, two fifteen-year-olds. Both of them were coerced into having sex with a neighbor woman in her thirties. Tony had never had sex before and felt helpless, used, and dirty. Chuck, who was more mature and experienced, thought he had a good deal.

And then there were Carla and Christina, two eight-year-old girls. When Carla's mother would rub her private parts in the shower with the excuse of making sure she was clean, Carla just thought her mother was a clean freak. She didn't like what her mother was doing, but she didn't think much of it. On the other hand, Christina, who had the same experience, felt invaded, confused, and helpless. She knew her mother was doing something wrong and didn't know how to stop it. She also thought there must be something wrong with her that made her mother do such a thing. It affected her self-esteem, her ability to trust, and her sex life when she was older.

We cannot actually climb inside the heads of other people to know what they are thinking or feeling, but we can ask, and we can make educated assumptions based on what we would have felt in the same or similar situation. It is important that you keep your empathy active and operating at all times in order to keep yourself from committing another sexual offense. You may have been unaware of what your victim was feeling because you were too focused on your own feelings and needs, used distorted thinking to misread what the victim was feeling, or shut off all feelings.

The following exercise can help you tune into the feelings of others.

Exercise 38. Thinking About What Others Are Feeling

After each of the following situations, list at least three emotions the person might have felt. You can use the feeling words at the beginning of the previous chapter to help you.

1) Doreen's husband came home from work and started picking on her. He told Doreen she was a lazy, stupid bitch, couldn't do anything right, and that he wished he had never met her. How do you think Doreen felt after her husband said these things?

mad hurt betrayed

2) Charlene's boyfriend told her she was the most wonderful woman in the world—smart, gorgeous, sexy, and generous. How did Charlene feel when he said this?

happy special loved

3) Elena worked hard on a science project for a competition at school. When she won first prize, how did she feel?

good proud confident

4) Petra's grandmother always hugged her and baked cookies for her. How did this make Petra feel?

5) Ilse's female partner always gets loud and obnoxious in the evening when she is drinking. How does Ilse feel when her friends came over to visit and have to listen to her?

embar ashame mad

6) Diana's husband is in prison. How does Diana feel when everyone is talking about their husbands?

upset   alone   mad

7) Amy and her daughter are on welfare, and most of their clothes are hand-me-downs. How does she feel when her friends talk about their new clothes and gifts and computers?

upset   not good enuf   ash

8) Aretha makes a lot more money than most of her friends, and she is able to go on much more expensive and faraway vacations than they do. How does she feel when she comes back from an expensive Christmas trip and everyone is telling what *they* did during the vacation?

succes   happy   proud

9) Kinita is the only East Indian student at her college. How does she feel?

10) Wilma calls Mary a "dirty nigger." How does Mary feel?

11) Gina overhears some co-workers making fun of how she talks. How does she feel?

12) How about when Gina hears her son's friends making fun of him for the same reason?

13) Some of Donna's friends give her a hard time because she is white and is dating an African American. How does she feel?

14) How does Donna's boyfriend feel when he finds out that Donna's friends are giving her a hard time for going out with him?

_____ upset   scared   mad_____

_____

15) Elvira's daughters constantly criticize her for what she wears in clothes and makeup. How does she feel?

_____ upset   shame   dishonered_____

_____

16) If it is the other way around and Elvira constantly criticizes her daughters for the same reasons, how do they feel?

_____

_____

17) Elvira's son Carlos finds a note in his locker at the gym that says, "Go back to Mexico, you greaser." How does he feel?

_____

_____

18) Frieda is a lesbian, but not open about it at work. How does she feel when her co-workers make fun of gays?

_____

_____

19) Jason's parents and siblings have gotten into all kinds of trouble with the law. When the local police stop and search him because he is a member of that family, how does he feel?

_____

_____

20) Because Roland is very artistic, loves to dance, and plays the violin, lots of people think he is gay even though he is not. How does he feel when he hears them saying he is gay?

_____ hurt   outcast   mad_____

_____

21) When people wrongly assume Rhoda is straight because she is feminine and enjoys fancy clothes, would she feel any differently than Roland?

_____

_____

22) Nanette was violently raped. How does she feel when her friends make jokes about forcing women to have sex?

_____

_____

23) Viola was molested by her father when she was a child. She didn't like it, but she still loves her father. How does she feel when her friends say that all molesters should be executed?

_____ upset mad confused _____

_____

24) Roger's stepmother molested him when he was eleven. He has never told anyone about it. How does he feel when his friends joke about having sex with an older woman?

_____

_____

Based on information given to us by both male and female sexual abuse victims, we can identify certain general feelings that most victims feel. Sex offenders usually aren't aware of, don't care about, detach from, or make a lot of incorrect assumptions about what their victims are feeling. Let's see how aware you are of what the victims in the following situations might feel. If you can't figure these situations out, pretend you are in a similar situation. Then think about how you might feel. It is important for you to be able to do this and remember it when you think about offending again.

Exercise 39. Victim Empathy

In this exercise, answer the questions at the end of each vignette. Try to give more than one response to each question. Think your answers over carefully.

1) Danny, who is six years old, was molested by his female babysitter. What are some of the feelings he might have?

_____ confused untrust _____

_____

2) Might Danny feel differently if his molester was male?_____ If so, why and how?

_____ *x'rem confused awkward* _____

_____

3) Judy and Jill, both teenagers, held Jill's younger brother down and molested him. What are some of the feelings he might have had?

_____ *embaras confused shame* _____

4) If Judy and Jill were adults who, with a male accomplice, sexually assaulted an adult male hitchhiker at gunpoint, how do you think their victim felt while the assault was happening? *confus. terrified*

_____

_____

After they let him go? *scared*

_____

_____

5) Jorge's ninth-grade teacher kept him after school to help him with his studies. While they were working, she began to rub his penis and scrotum. What are some of the feelings he might have experienced?

_____

_____

6) Naomi went over to her best friend Nina's house after work. They got drunk and Naomi passed out. She woke up feeling Nina's fingers in her vagina. How might she have felt? *disgusted embarassed*

_____ *betrayd* _____

7) Rachel was the foster mother of Domi, a seven-year-old boy. Domi adored her. She told Domi that if he pulled down his pants, she would make him feel good. He complied. Rachel then fondled Domi's penis. Afterward, Rachel told Domi that they would both get into trouble if the boy told anyone. How do you think Domi felt about what Rachel did to him?

_____

_____

How might Domi feel about himself?

_____

_____

Why do you think Domi didn't say no to Rachel when she suggested that he pull down his pants?

_____

_____

8) Ivy, an adult, went into a strange yard and peered in the bathroom window at a nine-year-old boy just as he got out of the shower. The boy saw her staring at his body. How do you think he felt? Shock, creepy

_____

9) Dr. Stanford, a skin doctor, told sixteen-year-old Hillary that she needed to examine Hillary's vagina, even though Hillary was there for a rash on her arms. Hillary undressed. Dr. Stanford came in to examine Hillary and rubbed Hillary's vaginal area. How do you think Hillary felt?

_____

_____

10) Penny, an amateur photographer, was doing photographic studies of children. She photographed Tommy, an eight-year-old neighbor boy, in his baseball uniform. Then she told him to take off his shirt and show his muscles while she photographed him. Later, she told him to take off all his clothes so she could have a better picture of his muscles. While he was in the nude, she photographed his penis. Why do you think Tommy didn't object? What was he thinking and feeling?

_____

_____

11) Joni, an adult, told her thirteen-year-old cousin Jessica she loved her. She French-kissed her cousin and fondled her breasts. Jessica loved Joni and wanted to please her, so she did not object. How might Jessica feel afterward? ashamed wrong

_____

_____

12) Clara fondled and stuck her finger in the vagina of her two-year-old niece as she was diapering her. It hurt the child, who had always loved Clara. What did the child feel afterward?

_____

_____

13) Jerry is fifteen. His mother has always cleaned his uncircumcised penis for him, from the time he was an infant until now. She told him it was necessary because he couldn't see where his penis was dirty and she could. What does Jerry feel about this?

_____

_____

When did this go beyond normal mothering and become sexual molestation?

_____

_____

14) Juanita showed her six-year-old son, Ike, how to masturbate both of them, and told Ike not to tell anyone what they were doing. How did Ike feel the following year when the Child Abuse Prevention program at school told the children that an adult touching a child's private parts was wrong?

_____

_____

15) Michael is fourteen. His stepmother got into his bed and touched his penis one night when she was drunk. How did he feel at the time?

_____

_____

How did he feel the next day when his stepmother was sober?

_____

_____

How did he feel when he told his father and his father told him he was a liar?

_____

_____

16) Harriet, an eighteen-year-old high school senior, and two of her male friends invited fifteen-year-old Ronald to a party. When he got there, he discovered that only Alice and her two friends were coming. They all drank some beer. Then one of the boys told Ronald that he had to have sex with Harriet before he could leave. When he didn't want to they made fun of him and threatened to tell everyone in his high school that he was gay. He obliged after Harriet masturbated him into hardness as the other boys watched. How do you think he felt at the time?

embarassed   pressured

Afterward when he saw them at school?

shameful & proud

17) Adair was at a party. He got drunk and passed out. He awoke, finding a girl he didn't know on top of him having intercourse with him. How did he feel at the time of awakening?

If he yelled at her to get off and she didn't?

If a male friend of hers put his hand over Adair's mouth and threatened him with a knife?

18) Miguel is ten years old. His eighteen-year-old sister and his sister's seventeen-year-old friend showed him pornographic pictures, masturbated in front of him, and then dry humped him. How do you think Miguel felt at the time?

When he was fourteen years old?

19) Brooke, a teacher, made six-year-old Joshua take his pants down in front of all the children on the school grounds because Joshua wet his pants. Everyone laughed. How did Joshua feel?

_____

_____

Was this sexual abuse? _____ Why or why not?

_____

_____

20) Darlene, a day-care worker, put her hand down the front of eight-year-old Raymond's pants in front of all the other children at the day-care center, and said, "Oh, what a teeny weenie you've got there." How did Raymond feel?

_____

_____

How would he have felt if they were alone on the center grounds and she was a stranger?

_____

_____

21) Joachim, a bartender, was required by his boss to wear tight pants to work. Rosie and Helen thought it would be fun to squeeze his balls. Rosie went up to him and did it first. Helen followed. How do you think Jorge felt?

_____

_____

22) Larry, an eleven-year-old, was alone at home one night when he received an obscene phone call from a woman. How do you think he felt?

_____

_____

Do you think he might have felt differently if his parents were home? _____

If so, how?

_____

_____

23) Moira is furious with her mother for having to babysit her six-year old brother again when she wants to be with her friends. While she is babysitting she hits the child's penis repeatedly with a stick. What emotions do you think her brother felt?

_____

_____

24) Jeannette, who is a twenty-nine-year-old mother of two, thinks she is in love with Jose, their fifteen-year-old gardener. She invites him in, gives him cake and coffee, and seduces him. What might he feel afterward?

_____

_____

What might he feel when he goes out with his fourteen-year-old girlfriend?

_____

_____

What might he feel when he finds out he has impregnated Jeannette?

_____

_____

Start here →

25) Now briefly describe your offense. What did you do and to whom?

_____

_____

How old was your victim? _____

Who was your victim—a relation, friend, or someone unknown? _____

Where was the offense committed? _____

Who else was there at the time? _____

If you committed your offense with someone else, who was the instigator?

_____

If you didn't want to do it, why did you go along with that person?

_____

_____

What were you feeling at the time?

_____

What do you think your victim might have felt at the time?

_____

_____

What do you think your victim feels now?

_____

_____

If you had difficulty with the above exercise or item 25 in the exercise, it may be because you have incorrect information and have formed *thinking errors* about how victims feel. People who sexually offend usually use these wrong assumptions or justifications to try to excuse their hurtful behavior so they won't feel so bad about what they did. The next exercise may help you see your own thinking errors and correct them.

Exercise 40. Thinking Errors About Victims

Below is a list of thinking errors or distortions about what victims feel. As you read over the list, circle the numbers of the thoughts you had about your victim(s). (Leave the lines beneath the thinking errors blank for now.)

1) He/she wanted it.

_____

_____

2) He/she liked it.

_____

_____

3) He/she would have said no if he/she didn't want or like it.

_____

_____

4) If the victim doesn't say no, it's okay to do.

_____

_____

5) It didn't hurt him/her.

_____

_____

6) It was okay because I didn't force him/her.

_____

_____

7) It was just a joke. Can't he/she take a joke?

_____

_____

8) We were just playing around. It didn't mean anything.

_____

_____

9) He/she was a prick/slut and deserved it.

_____

_____

10) It was okay because he/she was too young to realize what was happening.

_____

_____

11) It was okay because we loved each other.

_____

_____

12) It was okay because I was teaching him/her about sex in a caring and positive way.

_____

_____

13) All teenagers have sex nowadays. So what's the big deal?

_____

_____

14) Nobody was hurt.

_____

_____

What did you think about your offense that made it okay to do?

_____

_____

Read the Corrected Thinking section below. Then go back and write in the corrected thinking that applies to each of the statements above in the spaces following them. Pay particular attention to the items that you circled.

Corrected Thinking

Remember back in part I, when you wrote about your own victimization? Some of the things you wrote about how you felt as a victim apply to how your victim felt.

Victims do not want to be victimized. They don't want to be your "special friend," if that means you will do sexual things with them. They don't want to keep your secrets. Even when they don't understand what's going on at the time, they will likely be confused and angry and ashamed later when they do understand what you did.

They may not show that they don't like the abuse because they are afraid or ashamed. People who are drunk or who have been sexually active with others do not want or deserve sexual abuse. People should have control of their own bodies. Nobody has a right to do anything to anyone who doesn't want it. Nobody has a right to invade the body privacy of another person without consent, no matter how sexually active the person has been in the past or if the person has been a prostitute or hustler.

Often victims have a hard time saying no. Others may not have listened to them when they said no in the past, or they are afraid of being physically hurt or emotionally rejected by saying no. It is your responsibility to ask and be tuned in to what your potential adult sexual partner wants. "Tuning in" means being aware of body language as well as words.

Just because a sexual act is done gently or the victim is not physically hurt does not mean the victim has not been hurt emotionally. The victim may still feel violated, helpless, ashamed, damaged, afraid, and a lot of other painful emotions, and may feel this way for a long time, even forever.

Children are easily manipulated. They don't know enough yet to make good decisions about sex. They do not have the capacity to understand the consequences of what they do or whether they will be hurt or not. The same is true for victims who have mental problems, are developmentally disabled (mentally retarded), or are drunk or drugged. Even though children or impaired victims may have said they liked the sexual conduct (either to save face or because they liked the attention), they are very hurt or damaged by sexual activity they are not ready for or that is not right for them at that age or mental level.

Sexually abused children tend to feel betrayed, angry, used, dirty, scarred for life, different from other children, disgusted by sex, or may wrongly use sex to gain power as they get older. They also may act out sexually at an early age. In addition to the emotional harm, they may be physically injured if penetrated during the sexual abuse. Child victims often have severe problems later in life with substance abuse, depression, sexuality, etc. Even when they get pleasure out of the sensations they feel, the inappropriate sexuality leaves them feeling different, used, dirty, and sometimes at fault for consenting to or not stopping the behavior.

Once again, it is your responsibility, as someone who is older or more competent and knowledgeable, not to do anything to a child or impaired person that might damage him/her.

Many offenders think their behavior was a joke or just playing around, but their victims have been hurt and it is not a joke to them. Victims are commonly confused, embarrassed, humiliated, and feel powerless during these so-called "jokes" and "playing around." Some offenders either ignore or enjoy their victims' discomfort or pain, while others carefully initiate sexuality through grooming so the discomfort or pain the victim is suffering doesn't show right away. But there is still discomfort and emotional pain. No matter how gently the sexual activities are introduced, victims are left feeling used for someone else's pleasure without true consent.

When offenders look more closely at their behavior, they usually discover that they were feeling depressed, frustrated, annoyed, lonely, anxious, angry, or bored when they offended. They used their hostile behavior to make themselves feel better while making their victim(s) feel bad.

Common emotions felt by victims who know their perpetrators are embarrassment, confusion, anger, fright, disgust, violation of their person, and betrayal. Victims who are strangers to the abuser, such as victims of exposers or phone callers, are also often terrified of what this unknown person might do because the offender's behavior is bizarre and out of the ordinary. Will the offender find them, take them away, or kill them? And when somebody sexually displays themselves or masturbates in public, the victim is not "turned on," but usually feels helpless, disgusted, or scared, even if the victim tries not to show it.

Victims of rape or other types of violently perpetrated sex are particularly terrified for their lives. This terror may continue for years, even after the offender has been caught. Because of what happened to them, victims feel that they are not safe anywhere. They may also have nightmares, flashbacks, cold sweats, and a variety of emotional and physical problems.

If you have any questions about what the victim of your particular crime(s) might have felt, ask your counselor. He/she has probably talked to many victims of the kind of offense you committed and can give you further insight into what they might have felt.

The next exercise will continue to raise your awareness of what sexual abuse victims feel. But instead of writing, you can act out the different scenarios, two people for each, in front of the group.

Exercise 41. Empathy Role Plays

In your treatment group, act out the following situations with one or more partners. Decide who will play which character. Make up your own lines as you go along. Say what you think your character would be saying at that time. After each scenario, have the group tell what the characters seemed to be feeling and discuss what you were trying to portray.

1) A police officer questions five-year-old Jimmy about how his grandmother molested him. Show how the officer might treat the little child. Act out how Jimmy feels during the interview and about what his grandmother did to him.

2) Nine-year-old Dora tells her father that her stepmother is molesting her. Have her father at first think that Dora is lying. Then finally have Dora convince her father that she is telling the truth. Think about why her father would first disbelieve Dora and then be convinced. Think about how Dora feels when her father doesn't believe her, and then how she feels once her father does believe her, as well as how she feels about the molestation in general. Share this with the group.

3) Richard is an ironworker. He goes hiking alone in Yosemite. When he returns to his car, a woman is there with a van she tells him she can't get started. He fixes it for her and she offers him a cup of coffee, which he doesn't realize has a knock-out medication in it. He wakes up in the van tied up, with two women and a man sodomizing him and using a dildo on him. When they are through, they dump him nude out on the highway. Act out what he says when a concerned truck driver stops to help him, when he has to tell the police about what happened, and when the guys at work ask him why he hasn't returned to his job. How do you think he feels?

4) A police officer pulls Joan out of work and questions her about an accusation that she molested a neighbor child. How does Joan feel being pulled out of her job, what does she think the other workers will think of her, and how does she feel about being caught? What do you think the police officer might be thinking about Joan and this situation? Act that out.

5) Jack is eight years old. He runs away from home. A nice lady invites him into her house and gives him dinner. Then she and a man there say they are going to play a game with him. They have him take off his clothes and the woman rubs his penis and has him rub her breasts and vagina while the man photographs it. When they are finished, they ask his address and drop him off near his home. His

parents are angry at him for running away. Jack wants to tell them what happened but is afraid to because he thinks he is to blame because he disobeyed. Role play Jack and his mother. Have Jack finally tell what happened. What do Jack and his mother feel at the beginning of their talk? At the end?

6) Ben is fondled by his favorite female babysitter. He loves his babysitter, but doesn't like being molested, so he tells his mother. Act out what he feels when he tells his mother. Act out what his mother feels and does when she finds out what happens. How does she treat her son? What does she do?

7) Carolyn is a high school teacher. She has an affair with Jake, a male student. Another student sees them having sex in Carolyn's office and reports them. Act out what Jake feels when he is questioned about his activities with his teacher. Act out what Carolyn feels when she is questioned. Act out what Carolyn says when Jake's mother confronts her.

Did this exercise help you understand more deeply what the characters were feeling? If not, try the scenario again. Switch roles. Change your lines, and really get into your part. Discuss your character's feelings with the group. Did you really empathize with what your character was feeling?

In part 1, you wrote a letter to your abuser or to someone who hurt you in some way. Sexual abuse victims often write letters to their offenders as part of their therapy. It helps them express the feelings they have about the offense and offenders. Most of these letters are not mailed. Here is a letter written by a young woman to her older sister who had molested her when she was a child.

Why did you use me sexually? How could you have done this to me? I trusted you. I loved you. What gave you the right to use me this way? I guess I thought you had a right because you were my big sister. I just wanted you to love me, not molest me. You hurt me in more ways than I can say. You confused me. You made me feel dirty and used, like a piece of filthy toilet paper you then threw away. I was nothing more than an object to be picked up or tossed aside at your whim—a fool, not to be respected, only to be used and mocked. What did I do to deserve this? What was it about me that made you want to do it? I couldn't have been that bad. I never hurt you.

I have never been the same since. It ruined my childhood, made me feel different from all the other children. And as a teenager, the thought of someone touching me like you did made me feel sick. My view of relationships was distorted. You took away my value, self-worth, self-respect.

Thank God, I found a therapist who has been helping me overcome this because the effects of what you did have messed up my whole life, and especially my marriage. Didn't you ever think about what I would feel, what would happen to me afterward? Or didn't *you even care? Why? Why would you want to hurt me this way?*

I am so angry at you that it spills over into every avenue of my life. You have taken things away from me I can never get back—my innocence, my trust, my sexuality.

The next exercise in this chapter is also a letter, but this time it is a letter from your victim to you. Read the instructions carefully. Then sit down and complete the exercise.

Exercise 42. Letter from Your Victim

Imagine that you are your victim. Write a letter to yourself as if it came from your victim or your victim's parent. It should say what the victim (or parent) would probably say to you if he/she wrote you a letter. It should cover:

1) How the victim felt about the offense at the time

2) How the victim feels now

3) How the victim feels about you

4) What resolution or outcome the victim would like to see

5) Anything else you think the victim would want to say to you.

Think this through carefully. Make some notes first. Then write your letter in your notebook and show it to your therapist and group. When they agree it seems right, then copy it in the letter space below. (Use extra paper if needed.)

Dear _____(your name):

_____

_____

_____

_____

_____

_____

_____

_____

_____

_____

_____

_____

_____

_____

_____

_____

_____

_____

_____

_____

_____

_____

By

_____

(your victim's name)

Another good exercise is to draw a picture of your victim's face. What emotion was on his/her face at the time of the offense? And now? Draw them both. This exercise is another way of getting in touch with what your victim possibly felt and feels.

Now that you've imagined what you would say as your own victim, it is time to write a real letter to your victim—which may or may not be sent, depending on your victim's wishes. Your letter will make it clear whose fault the sexual abuse was, why you did it, and how you are making sure that you will never do it again. Making things clear is also called "clarification," and this letter is called a "clarification letter." The point is to make sure you really acknowledge your offense, understand how the victim might have felt then and may feel now, understand the damage you have done, and then make a truly genuine apology for your offending behavior.

For the final exercise in this chapter, write a clarification letter to your victim. The purpose is to help you take full responsibility and have full understanding so you will never do a similar act again. This letter is mostly for you (it will not be sent unless the victim has specifically requested it from you and it has been approved by your supervising probation and parole officer).

Exercise 43. Clarification Letter

Write a letter of clarification to your victim (most recent victim if there is more than one). This letter should include:

1) An acknowledgment of your offense (taking full responsibility for it, including a clarification that the victim did not cause the offense)

2) An acknowledgment of how you set up or tricked the victim

3) A statement showing full awareness of the harm you did to the victim

4) A statement showing understanding of the emotions you caused the victim to feel

5) An explanation of why, to the best of your knowledge, you did what you did

6) An explanation of how you are changing your thoughts and feelings so you won't commit an offense again

Write the first draft of your letter in your notebook, as you did with exercise 28. Share it with your therapist and your group. Rewrite it until they say it is okay and has no thinking errors. Then copy it here. (Use extra paper if you do not have enough space below.)

Dear_____(your victim's name),

_____

_____

_____

_____

_____

_____

_____

_____

_____

_____

_____

_____

_____

_____

_____

_____

_____

_____

_____

_____

_____ (your signature)

To prevent further sexual offending, it is important to remember what your potential victims are likely to feel before you consider any inappropriate sexual activity. Awareness of your potential victim's feelings is an important part of relapse prevention. It can help you stop moving down your offense chain and avoid or escape situations that can lead to future offenses. It is particularly important to remember the harm done to victims when you are at the Lapse point in your offending chain, when you start thinking about offending. Yell "Stop!"

to your fantasies about offending and replace them with thoughts of the damage you will do to the victim. When you see a potential victim, think about him/her as a person, not an object to be used. Really think about the harm you will do to that person if you offend. Remind yourself that you are a good person who helps, not hurts, people. Plan ways to get your needs satisfied that won't hurt anyone.

Summary

In this chapter on empathy, you had the opportunity to:

1) Learn what empathy means.

2) Increase your awareness of what people feel in general and what sexual abuse victims feel in particular.

3) Discover how people react similarly but differently to the same situations.

4) Learn some of the common thinking errors or distortions about their victims that offenders use to allow themselves to offend.

5) Appreciate what your victim might have been thinking and feeling.

6) Take responsibility and apologize for what you did.

7) Learn where and how you can use empathy to prevent reoffense.

Chapter 14

Self-Esteem

Self-esteem is what you think about yourself in your heart of hearts—not the role you play, not the dance you do or the mask you wear in front of others, but who you are when you look in the mirror and really *see* yourself. Your self-esteem can go up or down depending on what's going on in your life and how you think and feel about it. You gain your self-esteem from a variety of different sources—your parents, other family members, friends, and other important persons in your life, and from what you accomplish at school, work, and in your life. Your self-esteem was probably at an all-time low after you were arrested. Studies have also shown that the self-esteem of sexual abusers is often very low in general and especially right before they commit an offense.

In previous chapters we've talked about low self-esteem and how comments from others can trigger it. We've talked about how the negative feelings that come with it are a risk factor for your offending behavior. Building self-esteem is a part of learning to prevent reoffense, as is planning how to protect yourself when you have low self-esteem. Low self-esteem—that is, feeling crummy about yourself—should be a red flag, a warning to you that you are entering a danger zone for reoffending.

Now we're going to talk about how to raise your self-esteem by using self-talk.

How do you know when your self-esteem is low? Being in touch with your feelings will give you a clue. Usually you feel depressed, angry, frustrated, powerless, worthless, unloved, stupid, or any number of other painful emotions we discussed in the chapter on feelings and empathy. When you check in on how you are feeling, see if your emotions are connected to your level of self-esteem. You will usually find that your emotions and your self-worth go hand in hand. (Remember, what you say or do to others will have an effect on their emotions and self-esteem, too.)

There are various ways to increase your self-esteem. The most effective ways are through personal achievement (the result of successful, positive risk taking) and helping others. Personal achievements could be something like trying out for a sports team and making it or applying for a promotion at work and getting it. Can you think of some personal achievements or successful positive risks you have taken that increased your self-esteem? Or have you done some things that have helped others and made you feel better about yourself? Try to fit these types of experiences into your life. You will increase your feelings of self-worth if you do. One sure way to build your self-esteem is to live an offense-free life.

Your self-talk can also increase or decrease your self-esteem. For example, when you feel like you are worthless, if you say to yourself, "Nobody likes me, I'm stupid, I'm ugly, I'm a loser," you will feel much worse about yourself. On the other hand, if you say to yourself, "My best friend likes me, I am good at playing the guitar, I'm a kind person, I did something really nice for my grandmother yesterday," you will think better of yourself. Positive self-talk can include physical descriptions of yourself, reflections of what others think of you, and positive things you have accomplished.

The next exercise gives you the opportunity to increase the self-esteem of the person described.

Exercise 44. Self-Talk to Build Self-Esteem

Fill in the blanks with positive statements the person could have said to him- or herself which would increase feelings of self-worth.

1) Marylou's relationship just broke up. She feels like she is worthless and will never have another relationship. What could she say to herself to raise her self-esteem?

2) Tina's partner called her stupid and worthless. What could Tina say to herself?

3) Ginny just got busted (arrested) for shoplifting. She feels really worthless. What could she say to herself?

4) Bonnie started a new job, and some of her co-workers made fun of the way she dressed. She feels unpopular and unliked. What could she say to herself?

5) Word got out around the neighborhood that Erin was sexually active with lots of guys. She feels that people view her as a "slut." What could she say to herself?

6) Shelly's best friend found out that Shelly is gay and won't talk to her. Shelly feels worthless and different. What could she say to herself?

_____

_____

7) Rita has a weight problem. Her boyfriend caught her sneaking cookies out of the cupboard. Rita feels really crummy about herself. What could she say to herself?

_____

_____

8) Joan's spouse called her a "lazy piece of trash" when she was laid off from work. What could she say to herself?

_____

_____

9) After Cheryl got a promotion at work, a guy she worked with said she only got it because the boss had a "thing" for her. Cheryl thinks, "I only got this promotion because my boss likes me. I'm not really that capable." What can she say to herself instead?

_____

_____

10) Candy just said something really silly to a man she likes. She feels like a total fool. What can she say to herself?

_____

_____

11) Think of how you felt about yourself when you were arrested for your sex offense. What could you have said to yourself to help you regain your self-esteem?

_____

_____

In all the cases above, bad things either happened or were said that resulted in the people thinking badly of themselves. Sometimes nothing bad happens, or even good things happen, but we put ourselves down because we're so used to feeling badly about ourselves. For example, if you got an "84" on a civil service exam, you could say to yourself, "Most people got better grades than I did." You would be putting yourself down, and then you might feel stupid. On the other hand if you said to yourself, "Hallelujah, I got a good enough grade to be interviewed for a job on the second or third round. This was a really hard test, and I'm proud of myself. Even if I don't get a job with this score, maybe if I study even more, I can get a higher grade the next time the exam is given," you would feel much better about yourself.

Negative statements that minimize or discount the positive things you've done are put-downs. Thinking positively of what you have done—without exaggerating—will help improve your self-esteem. These positive statements are referred to as self-endorsing statements.

In the following exercise, change the negative self-put-down statements to self-endorsing ones.

Exercise 45. Self-Endorsing Statements

1) Johanna won second prize at the all-city art competition. She said to herself, "I didn't win first place so I must be second rate." What self-endorsing statement could Johanna have made to herself instead?

   _____

   _____

2) Susan fixed the carburetor of her friend's car. She said to herself, "Anyone could have fixed it." What could she have said to herself instead?

   _____

   _____

3) Rosita came from Mexico. She was fluent in English within three months. She said to herself, "I'm not especially smart. Anyone could have learned English in that length of time." What could she have said to herself instead?

   _____

   _____

4) Gianna refinished some old furniture. She said to herself, "It doesn't look professional." What could she have said to herself instead?

   _____

   _____

5) Lee cleaned her apartment up. She said to herself, "I don't know why I did this. It will just get messy again." What could she have said to herself instead?

   _____

   _____

6) Willa was asked to be in charge of the Christmas party at her church. She said to herself, "I guess they couldn't find anyone else." What could she have said to herself instead?

_____

_____

Think of a time you did something pretty well or were complimented and you discounted it. What happened, and what did you say to yourself to put yourself down?

_____

_____

What could you have said to yourself instead that would have shown appreciation for yourself?

_____

_____

Changing your thinking, as you have seen, can improve self-esteem. But don't forget that doing positive things can work even better. If you try to achieve some worthwhile goal or go out of your way to help someone less fortunate, you will probably like yourself a lot better.

Just how self-esteem fits in with the offense chain is an important part of the relapse-prevention puzzle. In case you haven't already guessed it, everything in this book is aimed at keeping you from moving down that offense chain to another sex offense. Let's look at how it works.

If you feel bad about yourself (have poor self-esteem), you are less likely to consider the negative outcomes when a **SUD** (Seemingly Unimportant Decision) has to be/has been made. For example, even if you have molested in the past, with poor self-esteem you are less likely to say, "No, I can't," when asked now to babysit. You fear to say no because you don't want anyone to think badly of you. You think they will like you better or approve of you more if you say yes.

But saying yes will place you in a **risky situation**. Because you feel bad about yourself, you are more likely to turn to the child, who looks up to you, for affection and sex. So you might **lapse**, fantasizing or taking that first step toward reoffending. It is easier to **give up** at that point because you already feel you are no good, and think, "Why not go the whole way? I'm already a loser."

In exercise 46 you will see how improving your self-esteem can help you prevent yourself from committing an offense, and how changing your thoughts or self-talk can affect your self-esteem.

What were you feeling about yourself (what was your self-esteem like) just before your offense?

_____

_____

What was your emotional state (how were you feeling) just before your offense?

_____

_____

How did your self-esteem and feelings affect your offense chain?

_____

_____

How did your self-esteem and feelings affect your offense cycle?

_____

_____

Do you think you would have taken the same path if your self-esteem had been higher and you were feeling happier, more satisfied, or more in control of your life?

_____

_____

Why or why not?

_____

_____

You can see from all of the exercises you have done that lots of different thoughts, feelings, and decisions contribute to whether you relapse and reoffend or whether you can succeed in your commitment never to offend again. Knowing yourself, the roles you play, and the boundaries you should honor, patting yourself on the back when you have done well, not putting yourself down, and improving your self-esteem can all help you to stop at any point in your offense chain before you reoffend.

Now let us review some of the specifics of what you have learned in this chapter on understanding yourself.

You can now:

1) Know more about the sources of your self-esteem—family, spouse or significant other, work, school, friends, and experiences.

2) Know how to check in on your esteem level.

3) Know some ways to increase your self-esteem:

   a) By personal achievement (or successful, positive risk-taking)

   b) By helping others

   c) Through positive self-talk

4) Understand how self-esteem fits into the offense chain.

5) Recognize how increasing self-esteem through more positive self-talk can prevent reoffense.

Chapter 15

Relationships

Another area where self-esteem is important is in relationships. Having good, positive relationships can help raise your self-esteem. Having good self-esteem can help you establish and maintain good healthy relationships, or at least know when to leave an unhealthy relationship.

In this chapter, we are going to explore the world of relationships—what they are, how to develop healthy ones, applying what we know about boundaries to the types of relationships we develop, and where friendship, sex, and intimacy fit in.

Relationships are often only thought of as romantic or passionate attachments. But according to the dictionary, a relationship can be any type of connection existing between people either related to or having dealings with each other. So you can have many kinds of relationships—with your friends, your children, your husband or partner, your parents, your neighbors, and even the grocery clerk or mail deliverer.

These types of relationships are not the same. A very loose and casual acquaintance with a grocery clerk, mail deliverer, or a neighbor is a very limited relationship that works just fine within its own boundaries. You smile and say "Thanks" or "Hello, this rain just goes on and on, doesn't it?" or "How are you doing?"

Friendship entails a little more significant connection, which varies in the degree of closeness each party feels to the other. Friendship is defined in the dictionary as "the attachment of one person to another by feelings of affection or personal regard." But there are both casual and close friends, as you will see in this chapter.

And then there are *intimate* relationships—which are extremely close. They may or may not be romantic or sexual, depending on the nature of the connection and the roles of the people involved. For example, you probably have an intimate relationship with your husband, if you are married. You may also have an emotionally intimate relationship with your best friend, a person you share your deepest thoughts and feelings with. But if that person is not your spouse, it is probably not appropriate for the relationship to be a sexual one.

People who have a broad spectrum of relationships, including close friends, live longer and tend to be happier and less likely to sexually reoffend. People without friends are more needy and may turn to the wrong person, such as a child, to meet their needs for closeness. With a range of friends, you can talk to your close friends about your thoughts and feelings when you are feeling badly about yourself and your life, instead of offending. Finally, when you understand the levels of friendship and have appropriate supports and boundaries at each level, you are less likely to inappropriately mix up sex with the friendship of a young child or a friend who doesn't want a sexual relationship.

Relationships should develop gradually so that both participants can build trust, starting as a very casual acquaintance and developing into a closer and closer friendship. Once you have a very close friendship, you may want to move further into emotional intimacy, which may include sexual intimacy if the person is an age-appropriate potential partner. If you move into emotional and sexual intimacy without a solid foundation of friendship, you are more likely to be hurt, or have your trust betrayed, or to hurt or betray the other person.

When you are an adult, children are never appropriate as either your sexual intimate or your best friend. This is because best or most intimate friends are people you can share your deepest thoughts and emotions with. While children may appropriately share their deepest thoughts and feelings with you, your deepest thoughts and feelings are not appropriate for children. They require a more sophisticated and worldly awareness than children have yet developed.

The diagram on the next page shows how relationships should build. Note that as you move inward at each level, you should be able to trust and depend on the other person more and more. If the person seriously lets you down at one level, you can just move him/her outward to the next ring, perhaps temporarily, until you work through your differences or disappointments and trust builds between you again. You don't have to dump this friend entirely—you know this person can be trusted or depended on at a less intimate level, for some things, but not for others.

Some people who have difficulty with boundaries (including some abuse victims) tend to meet a person and immediately take him/her into the innermost level, sharing their most intimate thoughts and feelings before they have any way to determine if the person is really trustworthy. If the person breaks their trust at that level, they feel that they have to throw the person out of all the relationship circles because there is no trust or connection on any other level to fall back on. This is a kind of "black and white" thinking, as if a person is either perfect or rotten, with nothing in between. It's much better to first have a solid friendship that becomes closer and closer and then winds up at the right level of comfort. You will be able to choose whether to move in closer or push the relationship out further. It does not have to be an all-or-none situation.

How Relationships Build

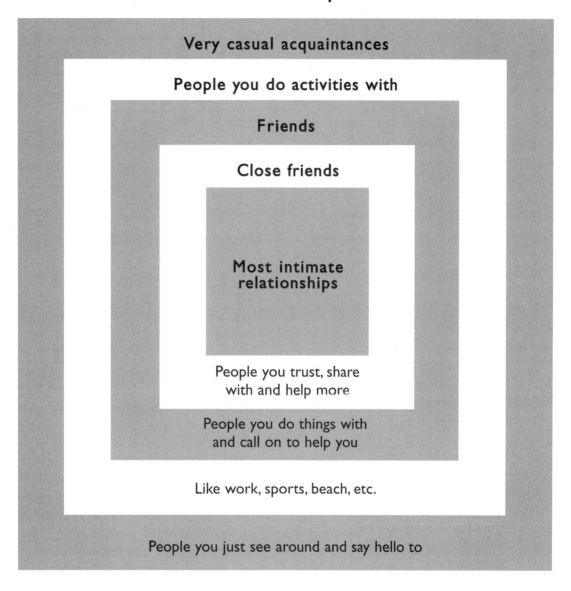

Very casual acquaintances

People you do activities with

Friends

Close friends

Most intimate relationships

People you trust, share with and help more

People you do things with and call on to help you

Like work, sports, beach, etc.

People you just see around and say hello to

Remember, too, that just because a person reaches the intimacy level doesn't mean that the relationship is necessarily romantic or sexual. Sex and relationships are two different concepts.

It is much more fulfilling if your sexual relationships are with persons who are intimate friends; however, sex with an inappropriate intimate friend can destroy that relationship—and in some cases could be criminal.

Exercise 47. Levels of Closeness

In this exercise, we will take the steps from the How Relationships Build diagram and turn them into categories. Write down the people in your life who fit into each category. (You may have more or fewer people in a category than the space allows.)

1) **Very casual acquaintances** are people you say hello to or chat casually with, but don't actually do anything with or invite home. There may be a lot of people in this category, so just list a few examples. Describe where you see them, or generally who they are.

a) _____

b) _____

c) _____

d) _____

2) **People you do activities with** such as sports, music, or work, but nothing much more than that. List them by first name and say what you do with them.

a) _____

b) _____

c) _____

d) _____

3) **Friends** are people you do things with, call on to help you, talk to about some things, or who ask you for help. List them by first name.

a) _____

b) _____

c) _____

d) _____

4) **Close friends** are people you really trust, share more with, help out, plus all the former items in the previous levels. List by first name and relationship.

a) _____

b) _____

c) _____

5) **Most intimate relationship(s)** are with the one or more persons you most trust, share with, and feel closest to in the world; your best friend(s). List by first name and relationship type (spouse, friend, parent, or whatever).

a) _____

b) _____

There are likely to be fewer people in each category as the relationship or friendship becomes closer and more intimate. Notice that your most intimate relationship may be with your brother or your mother and does not include sex. Sex is a separate element you may or may not include at whatever level you decide. If you and your prospective sexual partner are at the intimacy level, the sexuality is usually much more fulfilling and responsible.

So, who do you pick for an intimate, romantic relationship? Is it someone who looks sexy, turns you on? Is it someone who pays attention to you first? Is it someone who can give you financial security? Is it someone who shares your values or interests? Is it someone who likes kids or animals, or likes to party, or is a quiet stay-at-home? Relationships that have a solid foundation built on having lots of things in common usually last the longest and are the most satisfying. Yet we often pick our partners without ever thinking about what we would like in a relationship. In this next exercise, you will explore your relationship needs.

Exercise 48. What I Want in a Relationship

Part I

In this first part, brainstorm all of the things you feel are important in an intimate, romantic-relationship partner such as good looks, good sex, certain age, good physique, education, job, religion, financial security, family relationships, fidelity, sobriety, politics, values, loves you, loves your kids, is into some particular endeavor like sports or food or travel or music, is a good listener, can keep you in line, etc.—whatever you feel is important. Just write down everything you can think of below as fast as you can.

_____   _____

_____   _____

_____   _____

_____   _____

_____   _____

Part 2

Now look at your list closely and place each quality into one of the following categories that are listed below: those that are the most important to you, those that are important but that you could live without, those that would be nice but much less important still, and those that are really not important at all. Then write why each is or is not important to you.

Most Important Qualities

1) _____
2) _____
3) _____
4) _____
5) _____
6) _____
7) _____
8) _____
9) _____
10) _____

Why Each is Important to Me

1) _____
2) _____
3) _____
4) _____
5) _____
6) _____
7) _____
8) _____
9) _____
10) _____

Important, but Could Live Without

1) _____
2) _____
3) _____
4) _____
5) _____
6) _____
7) _____

Why Each is Important to Me

1) _____
2) _____
3) _____
4) _____
5) _____
6) _____
7) _____

8) _____   8) _____

9) _____   9) _____

10) _____   10) _____

Less Important Qualities

Why Each is Less Important to Me

1) _____   1) _____

2) _____   2) _____

3) _____   3) _____

4) _____   4) _____

5) _____   5) _____

6) _____   6) _____

7) _____   7) _____

8) _____   8) _____

9) _____   9) _____

10) _____   10) _____

Unimportant Qualities

Why I Can Do Without Them

1) _____   1) _____

2) _____   2) _____

3) _____   3) _____

4) _____   4) _____

5) _____   5) _____

6) _____   6) _____

7) _____   7) _____

8) _____   8) _____

9) _____   9) _____

10) _____   10) _____

You may want to reprioritize these slightly as you think about them.

Part 3

Circle the top four in your most-important-qualities category. Have your partners, husbands, boyfriends or other intimate relationships had these qualities?_____ Was that a problem for you?_____ Why or why not?

_____

_____

If you are not in a relationship now, consider waiting until someone comes along who has the qualities that are important to you. You are more likely to have a successful relationship.

If you currently have a spouse or partner or other intimate relationship, look at that person's qualities. Are some of them on your lists? If that person is missing some of the qualities in the first category, does he or she have enough of the second category to still make you happy? If not, what can you do about it? (We'll explore this further in the chapter on autonomy.)

Relationships and Appropriate Touch

There are many different types and levels of touch, from a simple handshake to a pat on the back, to closer hugging and kissing, to more explicitly sexual touches. Just like friendships, touch is on a scale from casual to intimate.

Non-sexual touching includes holding hands, putting an arm on someone's shoulder, patting someone's arm or back, giving affectionate (not sexual) hugs, pulling hair, and hitting (not all non-sexual touch is good or welcome touch). Sexual touching includes romantic kissing and touching, touching any private areas of the body, rubbing private parts against somebody, as well as oral sex, intercourse, and so forth.

It is important to know when it's okay to touch and when it's not and when a particular type of touch is appropriate. If you don't know a person, you should not touch him/her. For example, it is not appropriate to touch a waitress or waiter in a restaurant. Generally it's okay to shake hands with someone you meet or to hug a good friend. But you need to respect what the other person wants: some people like pats and hugs; others may not like to be touched at all. You have to listen, read body language (looks and movements), and not be afraid to ask what the other person would like. (This is also true in sexual touching.)

People will give you signals. You can usually tell that a person wants you to come closer if they move toward you, face you, or look directly into your eyes. If they are not interested in you, they may look away and change their position (turn sideways, cross their arms, step backward, and so on). Ask if you're not sure. Of course, some people may want to move closer to you that you don't want to be close to. Think of panhandlers on the street or in the subway. They often try to catch your eye and move closer so you will give them money.

And again, take notice—sexual touching of a child under any circumstances is wrong, harmful to the child, and strictly forbidden under the law. Even though a child may seem to crave sexual touches, **you are *not* to sexually touch a child**. That child is asking for affection and care, but has probably been molested and doesn't know how to get what he/she needs without being touched sexually.

If you have molested a child, you should not be alone around children. Even with adults present, you should never put yourself in a position to reoffend or where you have the opportunity to improperly touch a child (or an impaired adult). You also could be wrongly accused of improper touching because of your history of offending if you put yourself in a risky situation.

The next exercise gives you the opportunity to distinguish what is and isn't appropriate touching.

Exercise 49. Appropriate Touching

Part I

For the following situations, tell if the touching was proper or improper and why.

1) Julia had breakfast at Denny's restaurant. The waitress was very nice to Julia. Julia gave the waitress a hug as she was leaving. Proper or improper? _____

Why? _____

_____

2) Mary was introduced to Matt. She shook his hand. Proper or improper? _____

Why? _____

_____

3) Jane saw an old friend who had moved away. She ran over and hugged her. Proper or improper? _____

Why? _____

_____

4) Ali was talking with her friends. A sexy guy walked by. Ali patted him on the butt. Proper or improper? _____

Why? _____

_____

5) Lisa was babysitting eleven-year-old Liam. He complained that his shoulder was sore. Lisa offered to massage it. Liam said, "sure, okay," so she did. Proper or improper?

_____

Why? _____

_____

6) After massaging Liam's sore shoulder, Lisa asked Liam if he would massage her chest because she had pulled a muscle near her breast. Liam agreed. Proper or improper?

_____

Why? _____

_____

7) Toni ran into her old friend Dave at the mall. They hadn't seen each other for weeks. Toni gave Dave a light whack on the butt. Proper or improper? _____

Why? _____

_____

8) Sally saw a little child in the park all alone, looking sad. She didn't know the child, but she picked her up and hugged and kissed her and told her she would be okay. Proper or improper? _____

Why? _____

_____

9) Tammy's little cousin ran to her in the park and jumped into her arms. Tammy gave him a big hug and then put him down. Proper or improper? _____

Why? _____

_____

10) Anna and Tom met in person at Anna's house for the first time after meeting on the Internet. They sat on the sofa and began talking. Tom stayed on the far edge of the seat, away from Anna, talking but not looking directly at her. Anna moved closer to Tom and put her hand on his thigh. Proper or improper? _____

Why? _____

_____

11) Jackie was at a party. A man she had never met stared at her and began to move toward her. Jackie walked over to the man. They talked intently. She put her arm on his shoulder. Proper or improper? _____

Why? _____

_____

12) Jackie and the man walked outside. He continued to talk to Jackie, looking deeply into her eyes and standing very close. When he made no further moves, she decided she would give him a light kiss on the lips. Proper or improper? _____

Why? _____

_____

13) If Jackie and the man had walked outside for air, but he stood well away from her and kept looking around for his other friends, and Jackie surprised him with a kiss on the lips, would it have been proper or improper? _____

Why? _____

_____

14) Joanie was on a packed bus. She accidentally rubbed against a young man standing next to her. He didn't say anything, so she deliberately rubbed against him another time. Proper or improper? _____

Why? _____

_____

15) Mimi's nine-year-old niece came into the bedroom as Mimi was dressing. Her niece noticed that Mimi had some toilet paper sticking out of the leg hole of her underpants. She told Mimi, and Mimi asked the child to pull it out for her. Proper or improper?

_____

Why? _____

_____

16) Ten-year-old Tina had been molested by her stepfather when she was little. She lived in a series of foster homes afterward. Alma was babysitting Tina. Alma was sitting on the sofa and watching TV. Tina came up and sat on Alma's lap with her legs rubbing against Alma's crotch and she hugged Alma. Alma hugged her back, allowing Tina's

legs to continue to rub against her crotch. Proper or improper? _____

Why? _____

_____

17) Charlotte's eight-year-old nephew Joey had been molested by a female teacher. Charlotte wouldn't let Joey sit on her lap. She would only give Joey a hug in front of his mother, and then only a quick hug. Proper or improper? _____

Why? _____

_____

18) Ellen met Josh at a party. He enjoyed talking to her, but was not interested in becoming sexually or intimately involved with her. She kept coming closer to him, putting her arms around his shoulders, and brushing her lips on his cheek. He kept moving and looking away. Were her actions proper or improper? _____

Why? _____

_____

19) Imelda was taking care of her sister's toddler. The child was napping peacefully on Imelda's bed. Imelda loved the little girl and wanted to wake her up gently. Imelda began stroking the child's arms and legs, and then stroked the child's chest and crotch. Proper or improper? _____

Why? _____

_____

Would it have made any difference if the child was unaware of this, never waking up?

_____

Why? _____

_____

20) Carla and her girlfriend picked up a fifteen-year-old boy who was hitchhiking. They shared their food and booze with him. He asked what he owed them and Carla said, "You can just suck my tits," which he did. Was what Carla requested proper? _____

Why? _____

_____

Part 2

Now for your experiences. Tell of a time you touched someone properly and of a time you touched someone improperly and why.

1) Properly: _____

_____

Why was your action proper? _____

_____

2) Improperly: _____

_____

Why was your action improper? _____

_____

Remember, you too have a right not to be touched at any time or in a way you don't want to be touched. Whether touch is appropriate can depend on the situation and on the person, as well as on the relationship you have with that person. For example, it is improper to sexually touch someone in a public place. Know when it is an appropriate time to touch a person in a specific way and then whether or not the person wishes to be touched. Know when and how you want or don't want to be touched. And especially be careful when and how you touch children.

A Few Notes on Relationship Styles

There are thousands of books written on how relationships work. Here we can barely scratch the surface of a few styles we've seen among sex offenders (and non-offenders) and the balance we can aspire to.

Some people are controlling and/or domineering—taking power over others. That's one style of relating. Another is passive or submissive—letting the other person make all the decisions. A third less-than-healthy style is called "passive-aggressive," a way of controlling others indirectly, by a kind of emotional manipulation.

Any of these styles can be useful and sometimes you have to use diplomacy to get what you want. But using any of these methods to an extreme is unhealthy. If you find that your pattern of relating falls into one of these categories in the extreme, causing problems for you, it's time to make some changes.

If you always feel the need to control situations or exercise power over others, chances are that you feel frightened and insecure inside. The only way to put the fears to rest is to totally control what is going on, and dominate other people. This can interfere with healthy relationships because the other people don't have the opportunity to assert their own needs and desires. People around the controller often feel helpless or trapped, or they just have to leave the relationship.

The need to feel in control of others can be an underlying reason for turning to a child to meet sexual and intimacy needs: children are easily controlled. Sometimes the need to be in control can result in more aggressive offenses.

Think of a time you felt over-controlled and helpless. Was it when you were abused? Or was it a way of life in your home? It is not a very comfortable feeling for most people.

If you always go along with what someone else wants, you might have a "passive-submissive" style of relating. If you're a follower, you likely have very low self-esteem and don't trust yourself and your own judgments. You might be very afraid of being rejected, so you go along with whatever the more dominant person says. You might have believed that nobody else would really want you if you asserted your own needs and desires. It's tough to maintain a healthy relationship when one person is very dependent or even clingy.

Some women who relate in a passive-submissive way get stuck in the role of victim, allowing others always to take advantage. They may hook up with dominant, destructive partners who don't treat them very well because they don't feel they deserve better. They become involved in sex offenses by sitting by while a partner is physically abusing or molesting their children. Others do whatever the partners do or direct them to do, including substance abuse, child physical or sexual abuse, or other types of sexual abuse.

Another style of relating is called "passive-aggressive." People using this style look passive and compliant on the surface, but underneath they are rebelling. They are subtly resistant and angry inside. They may not even be aware of feeling angry, but they act it out in their behavior. Forgetting to do something you've promised, when you really wanted to say no is an example of passive-aggressive behavior. Acting out in a way that gets back at the person who is imposing on you ("accidentally" breaking something of theirs, for example) is typical of this relating style.

In terms of sexual offending, people with passive-aggressive styles might take out their anger at someone by sexually touching that person's child or getting that person's boyfriend or girlfriend in a sexually compromising position.

People with a healthy relationship style balance control and passivity. They use a diplomatic assertiveness rather than domination or passive aggression to get their needs met. They know when it is appropriate to take control of a situation and to what degree, and when it is better to give in to another person's wishes.

Now it is time for you to look at your own relationships and styles of relating. Complete the following questions.

1) What is (was) your dominant relationship style (over-controlling, passive-submissive, passive-aggressive, or healthy) in your closest relationship (present or past)?

_____

Do you think it has been healthy? _____

Why? _____

_____

2) If your closest relationship is not an intimate romantic relationship (not a husband, boyfriend, or other sexual partner), are you any different in these types of relationships than with an intimate platonic (non-sexual) friend? _____

Why? _____

_____

3) Is your relationship style the same or different in casual relationships? _____

Why? _____

_____

With your parents? _____

Why? _____

_____

With your children?_____

Why? _____

_____

4) What types of persons (over-controlling, passive-submissive, passive-aggressive, or a healthy balance) have you selected in the past for intimate romantic relationships?

_____

_____

_____

_____

5) Do you find yourself having a consistent pattern? _____ Is it functional or dysfunctional—does it work well for you long-term or not? _____

Why do you think that is? _____

_____

6) Describe what a healthy intimate relationship would be for you by answering the following questions and writing a general description.

Who would make the major decisions and how?

_____

_____

Who would control the money? _____

Why? _____

_____

Who would decide how you both would behave? _____

Why? _____

_____

Who would have the primary responsibility for your children, if you have any? _____

Why? _____

_____

Who would determine when and how you would have sex? _____

Why? _____

_____

Who would decide what you would enjoy recreationally? _____

Why? _____

_____

Who would determine who you will be friends with as a couple? _____

For you alone? _____

Why? _____

_____

Who would plan the meals? _____

Why? _____

_____

Who would determine who does what household chores? _____

Why? _____

_____

Now write a paragraph about what your healthy relationship will look like.

_____

_____

_____

_____

_____

7) If you are in an unhealthy relationship due to your relationship style, or if you are dysfunctional in some part of that relationship, what are some things you can do to change the situation? List as many as you can.

_____

_____

_____

_____

_____

Remember, you have choices in life. If you want to change things you can. It may be difficult, or the consequences may not be worth it, but you have that choice.

Some women tell us they just can't seem to develop or maintain a close relationship. Reread the beginning of this chapter on the relationship levels if you have trouble starting a relationship. Begin by talking to the people around you—at work, in the park, in the market, wherever. Be yourself, but don't be a complainer or a grouch. If a person appears friendly and interesting, ask the person to join you for lunch or coffee or some other activity and gradually build up to a closer connection. Don't rush it or you'll scare people off. Be careful whom you choose, so you don't end up being taken advantage of. Don't tell your innermost thoughts and feelings to casual acquaintances. Reserve them for closer friends.

If you can develop a close relationship but can't seem to make it last, look at the person you picked (is the person afraid of closeness or intimacy or unavailable in some other way?). Consider how fast you have gone (are you moving in too rapidly and scared the person?). Look at your relationship style (is it healthy?). Try again, correcting for any errors. The person you can influence the most is yourself. Make yourself an interesting, positive person and others will be interested in you. But remember: you have to sift through a lot of people to find the person(s) who will become your special friend or partner in a healthy relationship, but it's worth it.

Summary

What you have learned in this chapter:

1) What relationships are and why they are important.

2) Different levels of closeness in relationships and what is appropriate at each level.

3) How to build a successful relationship.

4) What to look for in an intimate relationship.

5) What is appropriate touching in relationships of different levels.

6) Healthy and unhealthy styles of relating.

7) Tips on developing and maintaining a relationship.

Chapter 16

Good Sex

Most women have sexual needs and urges. Normal sexual urges are not connected to anger or frustration or other painful emotions. They are simply urges that occur when you have a desire for sexual release.

If there isn't anyone important in your life, you may just want to masturbate. There is nothing wrong with masturbating. It is a normal part of healthy sexuality. Even when someone in your family or church declares masturbation is wrong, it is better to masturbate than to sexually satisfy your needs with a child or another person incapable of consenting.

It's not just men who masturbate. Most women masturbate, too, sexually satisfying themselves manually, with a vibrator or hand-held shower sprayer, etc. Just be careful that whatever you use is clean and has no sharp or rough edges. If you find you are doing painful things to yourself in the service of an orgasm, make sure to talk to a therapist about it. You are not unusual. You just have some issues you may need to work through.

It is important that you don't just go out and have unprotected sex with someone you don't know. As you are well aware, there are many serious diseases that are transmitted by "exchanging bodily fluids" like semen and blood. In addition, you don't want to bring an unwanted child into the world or have an abortion if it's not necessary. And then you might feel letdown or depressed if you have sex with a mere acquaintance.

You are responsible to yourself, your family (significant others and/or children), and to your potential partners about when, why, and with whom you choose to have sex. That means that if you do decide to have sex with someone you don't know well, you should make sure he uses a condom. And even if you know a person reasonably well, it's a good idea for both of you to be tested for AIDS before deciding not to use a condom.

Having the condom conversation with a sexual partner isn't necessarily easy, but there are ways to make putting on a condom part of foreplay. You can find ideas on talking about and practicing condom use at many AIDS prevention agencies, and workers there are not embarrassed at all about helping you protect yourself and your partner. Most AIDS prevention agencies and Planned Parenthood clinics provide free condoms, so you won't have to depend on a guy bringing one with him.

So what can you do when your husband or male or female partner is not satisfying you sexually? Communication is the key here. It is important to tell that person what you want, even show the person how you would like to be touched. You have a right to enjoy sex with an appropriate partner. So many women offenders we have known think that sex is all about satisfying the other person. It is for your satisfaction, too.

Likewise, if you don't feel like having sex, tell your husband or partner. You are never obligated to have unwanted sex. If you never want to have sex, however, you may want to see a therapist who specializes in these problems. Quite often, women who have been molested as children or who were raped are repelled by or don't enjoy sex until they have worked through their sexual abuse in a safe, supportive environment. It may be important for your husband or partner to join you in therapy to help you begin to trust and enjoy another person's sexual touching.

You are not crazy or weird if you don't like sex, want a lot of sex, or like to engage in less accepted sexual behaviors. The key to whether something is abnormal is whether it is dangerous to you or hurts someone else. If it doesn't damage you or hurt someone else, there is nothing wrong in trying it, so long as all parties involved are consenting adults. But make sure you really understand the consequences of any such choice you make. If your partner wants to try something that is uncomfortable for you, you have the right to say no and vice versa.

You can find a lot of sex on the Internet—on pornographic Web sites, and in sexual chat rooms, for example. While adult Internet sex is neither illegal nor necessarily unhealthy, getting hooked on it *is* unhealthy. It is easy to get over-involved in Internet sex, escaping from the real world by watching or writing and reading it. If you find yourself spending hours and hours online looking at or writing sexual escapades with great frequency to the detriment of your other, more healthy activities, you might be addicted to it. You will need to stop yourself, find substitute activities that are healthy, get into regular or sex therapy, and/or find a Sex Addicts Anonymous or similar twelve-step group to help you.

Child pornography is always illegal. Whoever made the images damaged the children involved. Having their images out there online, in DVD or video, or in print continues the damage. Getting involved in sexual talk with a minor online or in person, or looking at and downloading child pornography on the Internet can land you in jail.

Just to make sure you understand what is okay and what isn't, complete the following exercise and discuss it with your therapist and group.

What's healthy and what isn't? Why or why not?

1) Jolene is angry at her boyfriend, so she goes to the corner bar, picks up a guy, brings him home, and has sex with him. Okay or not okay? _____

   Why? _____

   _____

2) Is it okay if they use a condom? _____

   Why? _____

   _____

3) Josefina's boyfriend wants her to participate in a threesome with an adult woman they both know. Josefina doesn't want to do it, but she doesn't want to disappoint her boyfriend. Should she agree? _____

   Why? _____

   _____

4) Betsy is feeling "horny." She doesn't want to have sex with just anyone, so she decides to masturbate under the covers in bed, using a vibrator. Is this okay? _____

   Why? _____

   _____

5) If Betsy goes instead to a disco and starts touching her private parts while she is on the dance floor, is that okay? _____

   Why? _____

   _____

6) What if she masturbates in the living room while her kids are watching TV on the couch across from her? _____

   Why? _____

   _____

7) Miriam hates it when her husband touches her sexually. She goes along with it because she knows he deserves to have sex occasionally. What are three things she might do to improve the situation?

   a) _____

b) _____

c) _____

8) Gloria's husband wants to have anal sex with her. The idea excites her.

Should she agree? _____

Why? _____

_____

9) If Gloria is turned off by the idea of having anal sex, what should she do?

_____

Why? _____

_____

10) Fran has had three abortions. She doesn't like using a condom while having sex with her boyfriend and says, "Abortion is no big deal." Is it okay for her not to use a condom? _____

Why? _____

_____

11) What if Fran wants to have her boyfriend's baby, but he doesn't want any more children? Is it okay for her to have unprotected sex? _____

Why? _____

_____

12) Josie is in a committed relationship with Max, but she is tired of Max. She meets a guy named Ben at work and is very attracted to him. Is it okay for her to have an affair with Ben? _____

Why or why not? _____

_____

Does it change things if Max is sleeping around on her? _____

Why? _____

_____

13) Marla is feeling very sexual. She is not in a relationship and is home alone. She doesn't want to masturbate, so she decides to read a book instead. Is this okay? _____

Why? _____

_____

What will probably happen to her urge when she is reading?

_____

_____

14) Carolina wants to hurt her boyfriend while they are having sex, so she bites him. He likes this because it excites him. Is it okay for her to do this? _____

Why? _____

_____

15) Molly is tired after work and doesn't want to have sex even though her husband is feeling sexual. Is it okay for her to refuse to have sex? _____

Why? _____

_____

16) Toni wants to have sex, but her husband is tired and doesn't want to. Is it okay if she tells him he's no man if he won't satisfy her needs? _____

Why? _____

_____

17) If Dolly tells her husband that she wants him to kiss her and touch her breasts more before they have intercourse, is that okay? _____

Why? _____

_____

18) Melody fantasizes having sex in the bathroom of an airplane. If her boyfriend agrees, is it okay for them to do it? _____

Why? _____

_____

19) Lissette and her husband like to watch X-rated films before they have sex. Is that okay? _____

Why? _____

_____

What if the films show 12-year-olds in sexual ways? _____

Why? _____

_____

20) Maureen likes to get aroused by showing the neighbor children sexy pictures. She never touches the children, but later masturbates to her memories of what she did. Is this okay? _____

Why? _____

_____

21) Does it make a difference if the neighbors are seventeen-year-old boys? _____

Why? _____

_____

22) Moira punishes her husband when she doesn't get her way by refusing to have sex with him. Is this healthy? _____

Why? _____

_____

23) Della is madly in love with her girlfriend. She likes to have sex with her twice a day. Is this okay? _____

Why? _____

_____

24) Dana doesn't want to have sex with her fiancé until they get married. Is this okay? _____

Why? _____

_____

25) Claudia likes to have sex with her girlfriend Janine using their fingers but won't let Janine go down on her (have oral sex). Is this okay? _____

Why? _____

_____

26) Elena just got married. Even though she wants children, she won't have sex with her husband without a condom until they both get tested for AIDS. Is this okay? _____

Why? _____

_____

27) Artesa doesn't want to have children yet, so she insists that she and her husband use birth control. He is unhappy with this because he believes it is wrong. What should she do?

Why? _____

_____

28) Barbie's husband feels their sex life isn't exciting any more. He believes it will improve if they "swing" (have sex) with their neighbors. Barbie refuses. Is this okay? _____

Why? _____

_____

What are some other things they could do to spice up their relationship?

_____

_____

29) Gloria masturbates to an Internet sex program every night after work for two or three hours. She says she needs it to relax. Is this healthy? _____

Why or why not? _____

_____

If she writes back and forth on an Internet sexual chat room for the same amount of time, is this better for her? _____

Why or why not? _____

_____

30) Lorna, out of curiosity, has been looking at images of children doing sexual things on the Internet. She has only looked three times over a six-month period. Is this okay?

_____

Why or why not? _____

_____

31) What do you do when you are feeling sexual?

_____

_____

_____

Is that (or are those) a healthy outlet? _____

Why? _____

_____

32) What do you do when you aren't feeling sexual and your husband, boyfriend, or partner wants to have sex?

_____

_____

_____

Is that (or are those things) healthy? _____

Why? _____

_____

Homosexuality—being gay or lesbian—means that you are closest to and most comfortable in sexual relationships with people of the same sex as you. There is some controversy about whether people's sexual orientation (heterosexual or homosexual) is there at birth, or whether it is formed during their lifetime. Either way, for many people these preferences are well established by about age 5.

Many people have learned thinking errors about homosexuality that are based on an irrational fear. This fear is called homophobia. Homosexuals are no different from anyone else except that they are more attracted to persons of the same sex than to persons of the opposite sex. There is nothing wrong with same-sex sexuality, as long as you and the adult person with whom you share the sexual activities are both comfortable with what you are doing, and nobody will be hurt as a result.

Human sexuality ranges from total heterosexuality (exclusive preference for partners of the opposite sex) to total homosexuality (exclusive preference for partners of the same sex), with most people falling primarily to one side or another and some falling in the middle (bisexuality).

Being feminine or masculine in her appearance or body language does not indicate whether a woman is heterosexual or homosexual. The same is true of men. And just like heterosexuals, some lesbians have casual sex, and some are in committed relationships.

Some gay men and lesbians grew up with fear, guilt, or shame because lesbians and gay men are often treated badly by others, or because their religion says that homosexuality is wrong. Sometimes women who were molested are turned off by men because of the abuse they suffered, but they are not lesbians. Being molested does not "cause" homosexuality.

Another myth about lesbians is that they must "hate" men. Most lesbians do not in fact hate men, they simply don't relate to men sexually—and some men who expect all women to appreciate their charms are so disappointed they *think* the women who don't respond must hate them.

Some women who have been married or in sexual relationships with men discover later that they prefer women, even after they may have had children. They may have always preferred women but ignored their feelings because their families or their religion pushed them in the expected direction of getting married and having children. Many people can be aroused by persons of the same sex as well as by someone of the opposite sex. Some straight people have had sexual experiences with persons of the same sex. Many people experiment, finding out about their sexual preferences.

If you molested a child of the same sex, it does not mean you are gay or lesbian. Most adult child molesters that we know of are heterosexual in their sexual relationships with other adults.

We are not telling you whether you should approve or disapprove of same sex relationships between consenting peers. It is important, however, to recognize some of your thinking errors about homosexuals, to respect other people's choices, and to apply your empathy skills to what they might be feeling.

Exercise 52. Homosexuality: Judgments & Attitudes

1) **Personal Questions**:

a) Is there someone in your family or someone you know who identifies him/herself as gay or lesbian? _____

If so, who? _____

_____

b) How do you feel about that person or persons?

_____

_____

c) How do you feel when he/she visits and your friends are around?

_____

_____

d) What do you think that person feels when people make fun of homosexuals?

_____

_____

e) Have you ever had questions about your own sexual preferences? _____

If so, what have you wondered about and why?

_____

_____

f) Have you had any experiences with gays or lesbians? _____

If so, what were some of these experiences?

_____

_____

2) **General Questions:**

a) What is your opinion about homosexuality? (Okay, weird, don't care, interested, grossed out, or...?)

_____

_____

b) What is the basis for your opinion? (What was said by parents, religion, other literature, friends, or experiences?)

_____

_____

The questions above are not easy ones, and they offer a lot of opportunities for thinking and discussing. Again, an important question to ask is if the behavior is damaging to anyone.

Summary

You had the opportunity to learn the folliwing in this chapter:
1) That sex, love, and intimacy are different things
2) That both women and men masturbate, and it?s okay
3) The importance of responsible sex
4) Some information on sexually transmitted diseases
5) More facts about women and sexuality
6) That you deserve to have satisfying sex
7) That you have choices about how, when and with whom to have sex—or not to have it at all
8) Some information about homosexuality

Chapter 17

Dealing with Urges

Urges are one of the forces that drive your offense cycle, and one of the strongest urges we have (after survival and food and water) is for sex. Last chapter we talked about healthy sex. This chapter is about dealing with the unhealthy urges that lead to re-offending and a few techniques for dealing with them.

Often women who have been sexually abused either are turned off by sex or become very sexual, often equating sex with power. If either of these results applies to you, you probably should be working in therapy on your abuse—how you felt, how the abuse affected you, and how the abuse you experienced relates to your current sexuality.

We have found that a substantial number of women who have been sexually abused themselves have fantasies (daydreams) about sexually abusing their own children. Some act on these fantasies; others do not. If you have these fantasies, it is important for you to put a stop to them because you are placing yourself in a position of danger. You are on the third step of the offense chain, which is *lapse*. If you daydream about sexually abusing, it is easier to move down your behavioral chain to offending, especially if you are already in a risky situation where you have the capacity to offend. Remember, how you think about something can affect your future behavior.

Other female offenders fantasize about their victims, remembering the physical pleasure and control they experienced when they molested. Or they may relive distorted romanticized memories about their victims. Again, these are very dangerous fantasies for you to have because they can lead toward actual offending behaviors when your guard is down.

A very small number of women are attracted only to children and not to adults, and this is not just that they feel more comfortable and in control with children, but because they really are attracted to hairless, undeveloped bodies. Fantasizing about children for them is even more dangerous.

It is important that you learn to turn off these thoughts to prevent them from leading to inappropriate behavior. Tell your therapist about them and get help to retrain your sexual urges toward someone capable of consenting. In fact, any time you have a sexual thought that can get you into trouble, it is important to stop and change that thought immediately.

You can yell "Stop!" to yourself in your head and/or replace dangerous fantasies with fantasies of something unpleasant. These unpleasant fantasies can include situations you find embarrassing, repulsive, or fearful, such as things that might happen during or after the illegal sexual behavior, like someone you respect walking in on you while you are molesting, or being arrested at work or in front of your friends or family.

Exercise 53. Replacing Dangerous Fantasies

1) In replacing dangerous fantasies with unpleasant ones, you can use your senses of sight, smell, taste, hearing, and touch. Think of three unpleasant fantasies for each sense. (For example, for sight your example could be something that grosses you out, like looking at your insides coming out after being cut with a knife.) Make them as awful as you can.

Unpleasant Sight Fantasies:

a) _____

b) _____

c) _____

Unpleasant Smell Fantasies:

a) _____

b) _____

c) _____

Unpleasant Taste Fantasies:

a) _____

b) _____

c) _____

Unpleasant Hearing Fantasies:

a) _____

b) _____

c) _____

Unpleasant Touch Fantasies:

a) _____

b) _____

c) _____

2) Unpleasant fantasies can also be those that cause you to have an unpleasant emotion, like embarrassment, terror, or repulsion. They can consist of any object, person or group of people, animals or imaginary creatures, or any kind of experience. Let your imagination go wild. They can either be related to a potential offense or not. Think of three awful fantasies that might cause you to feel embarrassed, terrified, or repulsed.

Embarrassment Fantasies:

a) _____

b) _____

c) _____

Terror Fantasies:

a) _____

b) _____

c) _____

Repulsion Fantasies:

a) _____

b) _____

c) _____

3) Pick two or three of the most powerful of these unpleasant fantasies and write them down on a piece of paper. Every night next week after you go to bed, allow yourself to start having an improper fantasy. Yell "Stop!" to yourself after no more than ten seconds or before you get to offending behavior. Then read and focus your mind on one of your two or three awful fantasies. Really get into it. Feel the dreadful feelings or sensory experiences. After the first week, you will need to practice this at least once a week. Any time you catch yourself having an inappropriate sexual fantasy, repeat the same process. If the unpleasant fantasy doesn't seem to be working, try others until you find at least one that does work.

4) You can also replace dangerous or deviant fantasies with warm, loving, sexual fantasies of mutually consensual sex with a person of your same or similar age. (Developing relationships with appropriate persons of the same or similar age is an important way of changing deviant sexual fantasies.) In the space below, write out a healthy sexual fantasy. Describe the person, the place, what would take place before actual sexual contact, and what the sexual contact would be like.

_____

_____

_____

_____

_____

_____

_____

_____

_____

You have learned how to change offense fantasies and how to avoid and escape from risky situations related to your offending behavior, but what happens if you have a strong urge to sexually offend? Sexual urges, like any other bodily urges (hunger, urination, and so forth) do not have to be satisfied to go away. After a while, they gradually vanish by themselves. Urges are like waves, going up and down naturally.

This is important information because it means that you can wait out your urges or do something else until your urge subsides. You have a choice whether or not to act on your urge, and if you decide to act, you can choose whether or not that act will be healthy or unhealthy.

If you are having the urge or craving for an inappropriate sexual activity, you do not have to act on it. There are a few ways you can help yourself stop. First, you can make an Urge Control Contract of what you will do instead of or before acting on an urge. Second, you can carry an Urge Control Card with you at all times and read it to help you to either wait out the urge or remember to take the steps to make yourself safe.

The following are samples of an Urge Control Contract and an Urge Control Card.

Urge Control Contract

I, Dana Richards, recognize that I may sometimes have urges or fantasies to reoffend. I know that I am a valuable human being who cares about others, so I am making this contract as an insurance policy against reoffending. I hereby promise that when I have an urge, fantasy, or opportunity to commit a sex offense or any act close to an offense, I will do the following:

1) Stop or change my dangerous sexual fantasies by yelling "Stop!" to myself and substituting a negative fantasy of being arrested or humiliated at work.

2) Tell myself it is not worth taking any chances, I can **avoid** or **escape** a dangerous situation, it is never too late until the deed is done, and I can succeed in not offending.

3) Write out a good and bad consequences chart about reoffending or not reoffending.

4) Think about what needs I am trying to satisfy through offending and try to find some other ways of satisfying them.

5) Change what I am doing to something safe that will take my mind off offending.

6) Read my **Urge Control Card**.

7) Talk to a friend, counselor, or probation officer or call a crisis hotline (such as child abuse, rape crisis, and so forth).

8) Go someplace where I cannot offend (to someone else's house, to the police or probation department, and so forth).

9) If I still feel the urge and/or these alternatives aren't possible, take forty deep breaths, exhaling slowly.

10) If none of these techniques work, I will wait at least twenty minutes to allow the urge to go away.

11) Afterward, I will talk to my group and/or counselor about having the urge or fantasy, what I think were the causes behind it, and what I did to successfully overcome it. I will also reward myself for successfully following my contract by doing something positive I enjoy like going to a sports event, concert, bowling, or movie.

I agree to read this plan over every Sunday night as a constant reminder to keep myself safe.

Signed: Dana Richards

Dated: September 25, 2005

Urge Control Card

When I get a strong fantasy, thought, or urge to commit a sex offense, I will sit down and carefully read over the following:

1) A fantasy, thought, or urge to reoffend is not unusual. It doesn't mean I have lost control or failed. And it doesn't mean I have to offend.

2) If I feel scared or guilty about my sexual fantasy, thought, and/or urge, I will remind myself that I have power over them. I don't have to give in to them. I have other choices. I have other options that can satisfy my needs besides offending.

3) I will think of this as a learning experience. I will look at my life and try to figure out what has led up to the fantasy, thought, or urge. I will try to figure out what need I am trying to satisfy, and I will brainstorm all the other positive ways I can meet my needs.

4) I will follow the steps of my **Urge Control Contract**.

5) If I am still having trouble, I will think about whom I can call to talk to. I will look at the phone numbers of these resources on the other side of this card and call until I can talk to one of them.

Name and phone number of friend: _____

_____

Name and phone number of therapist: _____

_____

Name and phone number of probation officer: _____

_____

Crisis hotline phone number: _____

_____

Above all, I will remind myself that I am in control.

An urge or fantasy does not make me a sex offender.

I am in control. This urge will pass.

Now it is time for you to make your own Urge Control Card. Copy the card above exactly on a 3 x 5 index card, fill in the names and phone numbers, and carry it with you at all times in your wallet. Don't forget you have it there.

Your next exercise is to make up your own Urge Control Contract. You can use the format suggested below or change it to suit your own needs. Fill in your own name, your own negative fantasy, your own reward, and your own times to reread the contract. Also specify what places are safe and whom you will call to talk to or get help. Make sure you have more than one person to call plus a local hotline. The hotlines are important because you are sure to reach someone all the time. Then sign and date your contract. Remember: this is a way you can help protect yourself.

Exercise 54. My Urge Control Contract

I, _____, recognize that I may sometimes have urges, fantasies, or opportunities to reoffend. I know that I am a valuable human being who cares about others, so I am making this contract as an insurance policy against reoffending. I hereby promise that when I have an urge, fantasy, or opportunity to commit a sex offense or any act close to an offense, I will do the following:

1) Stop or change my dangerous sexual fantasies by yelling "Stop!" to myself and substituting a fantasy of

_____

_____

2) Tell myself it is not worth taking any chances, I can avoid or escape a dangerous situation, it is never too late until the deed is done, and I can succeed in not offending.

3) Write out a positive and negative consequences chart about reoffending or not reoffending.

4) Think about what needs I am trying to satisfy through offending and try to find some other ways of satisfying them.

5) Change what I am doing to something safe that will take my mind off of offending.

6) Read my Urge Control Card.

7) Talk to:

_____ (friend and/or relative)

_____ (counselor)

_____ (probation officer)

or call the _____ hotline.

8) Go to one of the following places where I cannot offend:

a) _____

b) _____

c) _____

9) If I still feel the urge, I will take forty deep breaths, exhaling slowly.

10) If none of the above work, I will wait at least twenty minutes to allow the urge to go away. Afterward, I will talk to my group and/or counselor about having the urge or fantasy, what I think were the causes behind it, and what I did to successfully overcome it.

11) I will also reward myself for successfully following my contract by

_____

12) I agree to read this plan over every time I have a sexual urge or inclination, or have trouble saying no to a partner, and even if I have none of the above, every _____ (day, week, two weeks, month) as a reminder to keep myself safe.

Signed: _____

Dated: _____

Summary

You learned in this chapter:

1) How to replace dangerous sexual fantasies.

2) The ups and downs of urges.

3) How to slow down and stop inappropriate sexual urges.

4) How to make and use an Urge Control Contract and an Urge Control Card.

Chapter 18

Coping with Painful Emotions

You've begun learning some ways to avoid or escape risky situations that might lead to reoffending. You've learned to think about others' feelings to prevent yourself from committing another offense. But the painful emotions that can lead to an offense can be triggered by ordinary life: an accident, the loss of a job, a death in the family, a hurtful conversation, the end of a relationship, even an abrupt change of plans.

Many women cope with painful emotions by either "acting out"—lashing out at others physically or emotionally—or "acting in"—hurting themselves. We talked a little about how these reactions fit into your offense cycle, but it's important to learn new skills for coping with painful emotions even when sex offending is not the issue.

Some examples of acting out behaviors are threatening others, hitting or slapping someone else, pushing someone into a wall or onto the floor, kicking a person or a pet, or using your position of power or strength to coerce someone into doing what you want.

Examples of acting in include using street drugs or alcohol, self-injury (including intentional cutting), not eating, binging (over-eating) and purging (purposely throwing up the food you just ate), not taking prescribed medications, or attempting suicide.

If you can't seem to stop yourself from self-destructive or hurtful behavior, or even if you can—just as a safeguard—it is important to find outside resources to help you. Individual counseling or therapy is the most important tool in the toolbox. There are also problem-focused therapy groups where everyone has the same or similar problems and the members are able to help each other. Talk to your sex-offense therapist about finding a counselor who specializes in your type of problems. It may be painful to work through your issues, but the results are usually very worthwhile.

There are also lots of self-help groups around, most based on the twelve-step Alcoholics Anonymous model. While they do not address some of the deepest issues (for those you do need a therapist), they can help you stop negative behaviors and maintain that abstinence. Among these groups are Narcotics Anonymous, Overeaters Anonymous, Gamblers Anonymous, Sex and Love Addicts Anonymous, Parents Anonymous, Take Off Pounds Sensibly, and others. There are even such groups for containing rage, overspending, getting into destructive relationships, etc. You can find them on the Internet, in your newspaper or phone book, or through your therapist or local mental-health agency. The larger your community, the more diverse these groups are.

Most communities also have hotlines you can call when you are afraid you might do a self-destructive or hurtful act. They are usually listed in the phone book. Trained volunteers can talk to you and help you cope. Among them are Crisis, Suicide, Child Abuse, and other similar hotlines. Don't be afraid to use them. Your conversations are private, and it really helps to have someone listen.

Additional resources include your spiritual advisor—minister, rabbi, priest, etc.—and family or friends (but be careful not to burn out family and friends when you really need professional help).

It's a good idea to make a 3 x 5 card to carry around with you at all times. This is similar to the Urge Control Card. On one side, list all of the resources available to you—your therapist's number, hotline numbers, self-help group sponsors or members, spiritual advisor, friends or family members.

On the other side, remind yourself that you don't have to act on your feelings. You can wait them out and they will pass. In the meantime, keep yourself safe by listing a number of healthy activities you can do instead of hurting yourself or others.

Make that card now.

Exercise 55. My Acting-In & Acting-Out Prevention Card

Fill out each side of your card as follows:

1) Front: Write down the phone numbers of people who can help you.

a) Therapist _____

b) Hotline_____

c) Group sponsor or member _____   _____

d) Spiritual advisor _____

e) Family member _____

f) Friend _____

2) Reverse: Write a message to yourself to slow you down and keep you safe, such as, "These feelings will pass. Doing something destructive won't help my problems. I will call the numbers on the other side of this card to help me be strong. I will deal with

just one problem at a time and not think about the others." Then write, "I will do one of the following positive activities," and list such things as, "I will call the numbers on the other side of this card, I will write a letter to God or to myself or to someone else, I will paint a picture, I will write a poem, I will go help my grandmother, I will hit a tennis ball against the wall, I will run around the block, I will make myself a pot of tea," or anything else you can think of that might help you.

Positive things I can do:

a) _____

b) _____

c) _____

d) _____

e) _____

f) _____

Physical activities are particularly effective in relieving depression and stress, so make sure you have at least one or two included in your list. Helping others in some way also takes your mind off of the destructive urges and makes you feel better, so include at least one of these activities.

It takes a lot of work, time, and effort to break negative behavioral habit patterns, so don't feel discouraged. You can do it. Don't give up. It will be worth it in the long run.

Summary

What you learned in this chapter:

1) Self-destructive (acting-in) behaviors have the same source as behaviors that are hurtful to others (acting-out).

2) Negative behaviors are the result of dysfunctional or inadequate abilities to cope.

3) You can learn to stop self-destructive and hurtful behaviors.

4) You can apply relapse prevention chains to keep yourself from getting into potentially dangerous situations and then hurting yourself or others.

5) It is important to have a list of resources and activities readily available to use when your risk factors are triggered.

Chapter 19

Autonomy

The next step after understanding oneself is to become *autonomous*. Autonomous means independent, self-sufficient, self-directing, and not subject to the rule or control of someone else.

Autonomous people are the ones who look strong and believe in themselves. They know that loneliness is just a feeling and it will pass, and even if it lasts a long time, it's better (though harder) to be alone than to be in a negative relationship. They know they deserve good treatment and they offer the same in their relationships. They think of others but don't allow others to run their lives. There are few things that will make them break their own rules for living. They don't settle for less than they deserve.

Most women remain in or return to unhealthy relationships because the thought of not being in a relationship is too terrifying to consider. While they are usually not forced into the relationship, they are too frightened of being alone to leave. They are not autonomous.

Marilee is one of these women. Her boyfriend Paul treats her badly. He dates other women, although that is not part of their agreement. He uses up most of their money gambling and drinking. When she complains, he hits her. "I can't leave him," Marilee says. "I love him. When he isn't drinking, he's kind and considerate and makes me feel loved and wanted." When confronted with the fact that Paul rarely isn't drinking, Marilee insists that Paul loves her and one of these days will change. What's really going on is that she doesn't believe she deserves better than Paul, doesn't believe a good man who is attractive to her would want her, and feels too helpless and inadequate to be on her own.

It wasn't until Marilee was arrested with Paul for molesting her nine-year-old daughter, April, that she was forced to leave Paul. And by that time, Marilee had lost her freedom and her daughter, as well as Paul. It would have been far better if Marilee had taken her daughter and left before the offense occurred.

The situation in Ginny's case is different, but she also lacks autonomy. Ginny wasn't happy being alone and didn't know what to do about it. Her sister had a daughter, Rosa, who was five. Ginny and Rosa adored each other. Ginny babysat Rosa when Rosa's mom worked nights. Ginny began to fantasize (daydream) about molesting Rosa. She knew she should stop babysitting the child because she was dangerously close to molesting her, but she was so in need of love and affection that she continued. One night, when Rosa wasn't feeling well and Ginny was holding the child in her arms, she gave in to her molestation fantasies. The next morning Rosa told her mother who called the police, and Ginny not only wound up in jail, but lost any future contact with Rosa.

Why did Ginny do this? She had no other sources for love and affection. She was unable to nurture herself, make herself feel good enough to find appropriate relationships, or to enjoy her own company.

Meredith had molested a child she was babysitting with her boyfriend, Carl. She was arrested, tried, and served a short sentence with a longer period on probation, including treatment among her release conditions. She was dating her ex-boyfriend's cousin Gordon, who was divorced and had his three kids over every other weekend. She would stay at his house only on weekends the kids weren't there. One weekend in October, Meredith arrived on her regular weekend, used her key to open the door, and saw the kids on the couch watching a movie on TV. "Where's your dad?" she asked. The oldest jerked his thumb over his shoulder and said, "In the kitchen."

Meredith walked through and confronted Gordon. "What's going on here? You just had the kids last weekend, this is supposed to be my weekend!"

"My ex's mom is in the hospital, what could I do?" Gordon said. "It's not like I planned this. We could still have the weekend, we just have to make sure the kids are entertained. C'mon, baby, I miss you."

"Can't do it Gordon. I'm already close to violating my conditions just by being in the house with them," Meredith replied in an even, calm voice.

"If you walk out that door, Meredith, you might as well leave your key, because you won't be coming back," Gordon responded angrily. "You're going to give up everything we've got because I'm a good dad?! I don't believe this!"

"It's not about your being a good dad. I'm going to give it up because you don't take me seriously enough to help me stay out of trouble with my P.O. And because your first response is an ultimatum, either break my conditions or the relationship is over. Okay, then. The relationship is over. Find someone else." And with that, Meredith put her key on the counter and walked out the door. She called another woman she knew and went to the movies and had dinner so she wouldn't be alone and replaying the incident over and over. Sunday she went to church and was invited to lunch afterward with friends she felt close enough to tell about the break-up of her relationship.

Meredith showed autonomy because she didn't let Gordon pressure her into bending or breaking the rules. She recognized the tactics Gordon was using as the same ones his cousin used when he coerced her into molesting the child. She wasn't going to give in to trouble again, even though it hurt to have the relationship end this way.

In the chapter on relationships, you learned that you can have all kinds of relationships at a variety of different levels. These relationships can keep you from getting too needy. And in the chapter on self-understanding, you learned the importance of building self-esteem. This chapter continues these ideas to help you become a healthy, whole human being—a woman who likes herself, who can enjoy doing things on her own, whose close relationships enrich her, but are not necessary to her ability to live a full life.

Prepare to head up the path to self-actualization—to being the person you want and were meant to be. This is your first step toward autonomy.

Exercise 56. Self-Actualization & Independence

1) This is your opportunity to transform yourself into the person you have always wanted to be. Think about the qualities that person would have. Describe her below. (If you can't think of what that person would be like, describe your ideal friend or the person you most look up to.) Cover the following topics and anything else that would be important to you that is changeable.

Intellect:

Education _____

Knowledge _____

Speech _____

Quickness _____

Talent_____

Other _____

Personality:

General effect on others _____

Humor _____

Industriousness _____

Self-confidence _____

Sophistication _____

Other _____

Relations with others:

Popularity _____

Fitting in _____

Respect _____

Admiration (for what?) _____

Other _____

Appearance:

Fitness/weight _____

Hair _____

Facial features _____

Figure _____

Other _____

2) Now for each of those characteristics, list several things you could do to acquire them. For example, if you want to be more knowledgeable in conversation, you could read newspapers, either in your library or online. If you want to be more fit, you could jog, or join a gym, for example.

_____

_____

_____

_____

_____

_____

_____

_____

_____

_____

_____

_____

_____

_____

_____

_____

_____

_____

_____

_____

_____

_____

_____

_____

_____

_____

3) Your assignment this week is to take the first step toward who you want to be. Pick one of these qualities and start to work on it. Report back to your therapist or group.

4) Now, just to make sure you've "got it," answer the following questions with at least three possible solutions.

　　a) Carla would like to be intelligent and well-read. What can she do to attain her goals?

　　　　i) _____

　　　　ii) _____

　　　　iii) _____

　　b) Toby would like to have a group of interesting friends. What can she do to become part of such a group?

　　　　i) _____

　　　　ii) _____

　　　　iii) _____

c) Ellie would like to have a high-powered job in the advertising business. What can she do to get one?

i) _____

ii) _____

iii) _____

d) Nancy would like to feel more confident. What are some things she can do to build her self-confidence?

i) _____

ii) _____

iii) _____

e) Carol would like to have a better sense of humor. What can she do to develop one?

i) _____

ii) _____

iii) _____

f) Norma would like to be more independent—not afraid to do things on her own. How can she become more independent?

i) _____

ii) _____

iii) _____

g) Darlene wants people to admire and respect her. What can she do to be the type of person people admire and respect?

i) _____

ii) _____

iii) _____

h) Evelyn wants to be less dependent on other people's approval. What can she do to rely more on her own judgment rather than that of others?

i) _____

ii) _____

iii) _____

i) Marlena wants to be able to enjoy life on her own, without a husband or lover. What can she do to increase her enjoyment of life on her own?

   i) _____

   ii) _____

   iii) _____

j) Myra doesn't want her children, parents, or partner to run her life any more. What can she do to run her own life without all the interference?

   i) _____

   ii) _____

   iii) _____

We are often asked the difference between healthy cooperation and responsibility and what is commonly called "codependence." Taking appropriate responsibility and helping and cooperating with one's spouse, partner, other family members, or friends are necessary to appropriate parenting, a good marital relationship, deep friendship, etc. It is when a person gives up her own identity, desires, and dreams, often with resentment, that the relationship or behavior becomes an unhealthy codependence.

Being independent, autonomous, "looking out for number one" (yourself), however, does not mean ignoring responsibilities, especially responsibilities toward your children. A healthy person balances his or her own needs with the needs of his or her children and significant others. This means she or he finds a middle ground where the important needs of both family and self are considered and successfully handled. And this goes for men and women. It's not balance when a male partner spends all his time either working or in recreation away from his family.

Parenting often requires a mother or a father to think of the children's needs before their own. Sometimes where your children are concerned, it is necessary to postpone the satisfaction of your own needs and sometimes you may feel resentment about it. This is natural. But remember, you chose to bring these children into the world or you chose to be with a mate who had children. Giving them appropriate care is the natural consequence of that choice. But it doesn't mean you have to totally ignore your own needs to care for them. That is not healthy for either the children or for you. Once again, you must find a balance that works for you—a way that you can have some of your own needs and desires met, yet still be a responsible parent.

In the next exercise, you will decide if the woman has gone overboard in either direction or has found a healthy balance. You will also have the opportunity to brainstorm what each woman could do to gain that healthy balance.

Note: Not all of the answers are absolutes. There is room for plenty of discussion.

Exercise 57. Autonomy vs. Co-dependence

1) Helene has three children under the age of five. Her husband works long hours as a machinist and never helps with the children. Helene never gets to do anything for herself because the children always need her. She's had it. She decides it is time to do something for herself, so she writes her husband a farewell note, takes the children over to her in-laws with a suitcase full of clothes, and goes off to live in a household of other independent women. Is this a healthy balance? _____

Why? _____

_____

List three healthy alternatives.

_____

_____

_____

2) Frieda has a nine-year-old daughter who is very beautiful. Frieda spends all of her time and money preparing for and entering her daughter in children's beauty pageants. Her daughter enjoys the attention. Is this healthy for Frieda? _____

Why? _____

_____

3) Lois and her husband are inseparable. Lois does everything for and with him. All of her interests are his interests. All of her friends are his friends. Is this healthy for Lois? _____

Why? _____

_____

Does it make a difference if she enjoys all of this? _____

Why? _____

_____

4) Antoinette prides herself on being her own person. Her eleven-year-old son is in a play at school and wants her to come see it. She tells him she can't because she has planned to spend the day visiting with an old friend. Is this a healthy balance? _____

Why? _____

_____

Would it make a difference if she hasn't seen the friend for ten years? _____

Why? _____

_____

5) Vunita wants to work, but her husband is opposed to it because he is making a good living and wants her to stay home and take care of the house. Vunita accepts a job as an elementary school teacher.

Is this healthy for Vunita? _____

Why? _____

_____

6) Marla wants to go to college to earn her degree. Her children are in preschool and elementary school. Her husband wants her to put off college until the children graduate from high school. Should Marla follow her husband's wishes? _____

Why? _____

_____

If she decides to go to college, how can she best accommodate both her own needs and her responsibilities to the children and her husband?

_____

_____

7) Johanna's lover Hilda wants her to go with her to her brother's wedding in Ohio. She would like to stay home and have fun while she is gone. What should she do?

_____

_____

Why? _____

_____

If her partner's brother and family always ignore and snub her, would that make a difference? _____

Why? _____

_____

8) Carole is a single mom. She is offered a top executive position in an out-of-state company. Her children don't want to leave their friends. Is it healthy if she moves with them to take the job? _____

Why? _____

_____

What if she takes the job, but leaves the children with her ex-husband? Is that healthy? _____

Why? _____

_____

Is it healthy if she turns down the job and stays in her old job? _____

Why? _____

_____

9) Jill and her boyfriend are into drugs. She wants to stop using by entering a residential drug program. Her boyfriend says he needs her to stay home and care for their kids. What should she do?

_____

_____

Why? _____

_____

If she enters the drug program, what should she do with her children? (Think of several possible solutions.)

_____

_____

_____

10) Mathilda enjoys drinking a lot. Her partner Leona has gone on the wagon and wants her to stop drinking, too, and to throw out all the liquor in the house. She refuses. Is this healthy? _____

Why? _____

_____

11) Judy, a single mother with three young children, falls in love with Roger, who had previously been in prison for child molestation. She decides to marry him because he swears he will never molest her children. Is this healthy? _____

Why? _____

_____

Would your answer be any different if his molestations occurred almost twenty years before and he has completed an extensive sexual abuse treatment program? _____

Why? _____

_____

If she marries him and retains custody of her children, list five things she could do to keep them as safe as possible.

_____

_____

_____

_____

_____

Being alone and being lonely are two different concepts. A person is alone when she is by herself, separate or apart from others. There is no emotional component attached to being alone. It can be fun, fulfilling, depressing, or any number of other feelings. On the other hand, loneliness is defined as the state of feeling depressed at being alone.

Just because you are alone doesn't mean you have to feel lonely. There are things you can do to help yourself. You can learn to enjoy your own company. You can build a circle of friends around yourself. You can do things that make you feel fulfilled, such as reading, doing artwork, participating in a sport, going to the movies, doing yoga, going to church, or other activities that you enjoy. You can devote some time to helping others, such as the elderly, disabled, or poor. All of these things will help you to be autonomous and independent, and you will not need to rely on an unhealthy relationship to make you feel whole.

Exercise 58. Being Alone but Not Lonely

Part 1

What are some of the things you enjoy doing by yourself? Check off all of the following things you enjoy doing alone, then add some others of your own.

_____ Watching TV

_____ Listening to music

_____ Reading

_____ Eating

_____ Using drugs

_____ Shopping

_____ Exercising

_____ Taking a bath or shower

_____ Masturbating

_____ Doing the crossword puzzle

_____ Watching pornography

_____ Drinking alcoholic beverages

_____ Going to the movies

_____ Dancing around the house

_____ Hiking in the wilderness

_____ Driving a car

_____ Going to a restaurant

_____ Going to a bar

_____ Vacationing

_____ Making things

_____ Other things _____

_____ Doing artwork_____

_____ Cooking _____

_____ Playing a musical instrument _____

_____ Studying _____

Now put an X through all of the items above that are unhealthy. Circle the items that are healthy. Then write them down below and tell why they are healthy.

_____

_____

_____

_____

_____

_____

_____

Part 2

In the next part of the exercise, list ways to help each of the following women.

1) Jill is hungry and would like to go out and have a delicious dinner at a good restaurant. None of her friends are available to go with her. What can she do to motivate herself to go out to the restaurant alone and enjoy a dinner by herself?

_____

_____

_____

2) Norene is alone now that her husband has left her and her children have moved out. Her car is in the shop, there is no public transportation, and her friends are all too busy to come by. What can she do to have a good time by herself?

_____

_____

_____

3) When her car is fixed, and Norene can go out, what are some activities she might enjoy doing on her own?

_____

_____

_____

4) Eva has just kicked her no-good, lazy boyfriend out, and she is on her own. Now, even though he was terrible company, she feels lonely. What are some things she can do to help herself feel less lonely?

_____

_____

_____

5) What are some things you can do for yourself to help you feel less lonely when you are alone?

_____

_____

_____

_____

_____

Part 3

Now is your opportunity to practice being alone without feeling lonely. This is a four-week assignment. Each week, you are to do the activities listed and answer the questions relative to them.

Week 1: Go to a movie, play, or concert alone. Afterward answer the following questions.

1) Where did you go?

_____

2) Did you enjoy the movie, play, or concert? _____

Why or why not? _____

3) How did it feel waiting alone to buy the ticket and entering?

_____

4) Did you run into anyone you knew?_____

If so, how did it make you feel being there alone?

_____

5) Was the overall experience an enjoyable one? _____

Why? _____

If you didn't enjoy it, felt lonely or uncomfortable, that's okay, that's normal. Try it a few more times. You may get over your loneliness or discomfort once it becomes more of a common practice for you.

Week 2: Go out to dinner by yourself. Then answer these questions.

1) Where did you go?

_____

2) Did you enjoy the meal? _____

Why or why not? _____

3) Did you run into anyone you knew? _____

If so, how did it make you feel being there alone?

_____

4) How did you entertain yourself while you were there? Did you…

_____ Read a book, magazine, or newspaper

_____ Talk to other diners

_____ Talk to the wait staff

_____ Just savor the taste of the food

_____ Other: (list) _____

As with the first assignment, if you didn't enjoy it, felt lonely or uncomfortable, try it a few more times to get over your loneliness or discomfort as it becomes more of a common practice for you.

Week 3: Stay at home by yourself for twenty-four hours—one whole day and night. Plan your home-alone day for a time when anyone who lives with you is staying elsewhere (roommate sleeping at a boyfriend or girlfriend's, spouse or partner away on business or visiting family). Afterward answer these questions.

1) What did you do to entertain yourself during this time?

_____

Were these things healthy or unhealthy (or both)? _____

Why? _____

(If you did unhealthy things, do this exercise again, without doing unhealthy things.)

2) How did you feel being alone for this day and night?

_____

_____

3) What could you do in the future to improve on this experience?

_____

_____

Week 4: Take a trip somewhere by yourself. It doesn't have to be far away. Stay overnight. (Some of you who are on parole or probation may not be allowed to do this part of the exercise. If you are under supervision, ask your parole or probation officer for permission. If your request is denied, save this portion of the exercise until you are off probation or parole. In the meantime, imagine where you would go, and visualize each step and how you think you would feel. It will be interesting to compare the two when you are able to go.)

1) Where did you go?

_____

2) Why did you select that place?

_____

3) What did you do there?

_____

4) How did you feel most of the time?

_____

5) Why do think that was?

_____

6) Is there anything you could do in the future to make any experience like this more enjoyable? _____

What?

_____

_____

While a healthy person enjoys her own company and can find activities that she does by herself pleasurable, she also has friends and relationships at many different levels, from mere acquaintances to intimate friends and lovers. It is the balance between being alone and being with others that is the positive place to be.

Can you remember at what point in the spectrum you were when you committed or participated in your sex offense(s)? Think about it. Were you dependent on someone else? Or were you a loner without adult support in your life? Find a good balance for yourself now.

Summary

In this chapter you learned:

1) The meaning of *autonomy*

2) How over-dependence or being a loner can lead to (re)offense

3) Ways of self actualizing—being the person you want to be

4) The difference between healthy cooperation and codependence

5) The difference between being alone and lonely

6) Ways to enjoy your own company

Chapter 20

Assertiveness and Healthy Communication

Good communication and assertiveness skills are major tools for a healthy, non-offending lifestyle.

Communication means sharing information with other people either with written or spoken words or by behaviors and physical gestures (such as shrugging your shoulders to say, "I don't know"). Communication has three parts: verbal expression, nonverbal expression, and perception (listening/observing).

Verbal expression simply means using words to express your thoughts and feelings. These words can be spoken or written. They can also be direct or indirect. For example, telling somebody something or writing them a letter is direct verbal communication. Writing a play or poem, or talking to someone other than the person to whom the communication is directed are forms of indirect verbal communication. Not quite saying what you mean (saying, "The wood box is empty," when you mean, "Please go bring in some wood," for example) is also indirect verbal communication.

Nonverbal expression means using something other than words to express yourself. For example, body language—the expression on your face or the position of your shoulders or hands can tell others how you are feeling. If you are feeling sad, usually your face will look unhappy, you might look at the floor, your shoulders slump, your hands hang or might be clenched against your body, and your walk may be kind of slow and draggy. If you are feeling happy, you are more likely to have a smile on your face, stand straighter, look up and out, and walk with more energy.

Other types of nonverbal expression are things you do (behaviors), such as hitting something or someone or kissing a special friend. Hitting communicates anger or frustration, while kissing communicates positive feelings toward that person. Those are direct nonverbal expressions. Hugs, pats, turning your back, covering your ears, yawning, and other forms of physical expression are also nonverbal.

Other things you might do, such as painting or baking, can *indirectly* communicate to someone what you are thinking and feeling. For example, if you paint a droopy tree in blues and greens, you may be communicating that you are feeling sad, or if you bake a cake for someone's birthday, you may be communicating your love and care for that person. On the other hand, you could be communicating that you feel guilty because you have been neglecting the birthday friend. Notice that other people can't interpret nonverbal *indirect* expression nearly as accurately as they can *direct* expression.

When you committed your sex offense, you were communicating. Think about what you were communicating, both in your feelings and thoughts. Who were you communicating with? Was it verbal or nonverbal or some of both? Was it direct or indirect communication? Who should your message really have been directed to? How could you communicate this message in a non-hurtful way?

Some of the female offenders we have worked with have molested their stepchildren, children they have been forced to babysit, or other children because they felt angry, frustrated, and/or powerless in their situation. They were communicating their feelings in an indirect and unacceptable way.

Camilla had terrible acne, a receding chin, and was very tall and thin. She had no real friends and had never had a boyfriend, though she would have liked to. She worked in a center for disabled children. One day she helped Eugene, who had cerebral palsy, go to the bathroom. After she helped him pull his pants down, she began to fondle his penis. She was indirectly communicating her need for intimacy and her feelings of inadequacy about herself. She was saying in her actions that she didn't believe any adult would love her.

Now is your turn to write down what, to whom, and how you were communicating when you committed your sex offense.

Exercise 59. Communication & Your Offense

Think through and answer the following questions. If you are having trouble, ask your therapist or group members for help.

1) What do you think you might have been communicating by committing your sex offense? (You may have simply been communicating your feelings, or you may have been communicating multiple things. For example, communicating to your partner in the crime that you cared for him more than the victim, telling yourself and your victim that you were in control and powerful, and/or communicating your powerlessness to stop the abuse when you knew it was wrong.)

_____

_____

_____

_____

2) Who were you communicating with? (Answer this for each communication. This can include yourself, your partner, your victim, your abuser, your family, society in general, or all of them.)

_____

_____

_____

_____

_____

3) Was your communication verbal, nonverbal, or some of both? _____

What part was verbal?

_____

What part was nonverbal?

_____

4) Was it direct or indirect communication, or both? _____

What part was direct?

_____

What part was indirect?

_____

5) Who should your message really have been directed to? (This can be more than one person, such as yourself, your mother, etc.)

_____

6) How could you communicate this message in a non-hurtful way? Think of at least four ways. (You may need to read ahead to the section on healthy communications to help you answer this question.)

a) _____

b) _____

c) _____

d) _____

Communication can be healthy or unhealthy. For example, when you scream and swear at someone or call them names, the communication is not a healthy one. When you talk out your problems and feelings more calmly, it is healthy (unless you are using an inappropriate person to talk to, such as a stranger or a child). When you cut on yourself, punch the wall, or punch someone else, you are expressing yourself in an unhealthy, unproductive way. But if you write down or draw your feelings or do some physical exercise, like jogging, to express them, your actions will help you express your feelings in a healthy and productive way.

When you use positive ways to communicate your thoughts and feelings, you are more likely to stay offense-free and to maintain the balanced, healthy life you are building.

The following exercise is designed to help you choose and practice healthy communication and to help you understand the difference between what is productive and positive, and what is dysfunctional and negative.

Exercise 60. Healthy & Unhealthy Communication

Part I

For each of the following situations, write down whether communication was healthy or unhealthy, and why.

1) Jody's older brother made fun of her all the time. She went to him one day and told him how bad it made her feel. Was this healthy or unhealthy? _____

   Why? _____

2) Donna got blamed for an error someone else made at work. Her supervisor wouldn't listen to her when she tried to explain, so she wrote a letter to the supervisor and explained the situation. Was this healthy or unhealthy? _____

   Why? _____

3) Rosa's son yelled at her, so she yelled back. Was this healthy or unhealthy? _____

   Why? _____

4) Jolene's husband was always hollering at her. She felt like she couldn't talk to him, so she made a fist and threatened to hit his five-year-old son if he didn't shut up. Was this healthy or unhealthy? _____

   Why? _____

   What kind of communication was this? Direct or indirect expression, verbal or non-verbal?

   _____

5) Amelia's ex-husband Floyd was a drug user who spent her savings account and maxed out all of their charge cards. Amelia was furious at him, but he disappeared so she couldn't tell him how she felt. Amelia took a photo she had of him and punched it in the nose, stomped on it, and crumpled it up. Was this healthy or unhealthy?

_____

Why? _____

What kind of communication was it?

_____

One day, Floyd showed up at the door, and said he needed someplace to stay. Amelia slammed the door in his face and threw all of his possessions out the window, breaking his stereo, radio, and a framed photo of his parents. Was this healthy or unhealthy?

_____

Why? _____

6) Briana's uncle raped her when she was eighteen years old. Her uncle denied it when confronted by the family. Briana felt enraged, frustrated, and powerless. She signed up for a karate class and practiced every day. Was this healthy or healthy? _____

Why? _____

If Briana had slapped a really nasty coworker at her job instead, would that have been healthy or unhealthy? _____

Why? _____

What type of communication would it have been? _____

7) Miriam felt that her partner, Louise never listened to her any more. She was feeling depressed and misunderstood. She went into her room and stayed there, thinking over and over that nobody cared about her. She didn't want to talk to anybody. Was this healthy or unhealthy? _____

Why? _____

If she had gone to the local bar and picked up a woman instead, would that have been healthy or unhealthy? _____

Why? _____

8) Delia had dreams about molesting her children. She never told anyone about them. Was this healthy or unhealthy? _____

Why? _____

9) Molly was thinking about what it would feel like to touch the penis of her friend's eleven-year-old son. She talked to her sister about what she was feeling. Was this healthy or unhealthy? _____

Why? _____

If, instead, she had talked to the eleven-year-old, would that have been healthy or unhealthy? _____

Why? _____

10) Belle played sad songs on her guitar whenever she felt frustrated. Was this healthy or unhealthy? _____

Why? _____

Part 2

For the following situations, write down a healthy way the person could communicate her feelings and thoughts. It could be verbal or nonverbal, direct or indirect.

1) Marni's mother molested her when she was a child. Her mother was caught, and then moved back to Canada where she had originally come from. Marni didn't like what her mother had done, but she still loved and missed her. As an adult, Marni wanted her mother to know her feelings, both of love and betrayal. Marni does not have the funds to visit her mother, and her mother doesn't have a telephone. How can Marni communicate her feelings?

_____

_____

2) Tilly's brother and sister-in-law won't speak to her since she molested their son (her nephew). They got a restraining order, so she is not even allowed to write to them. How can she express her feelings of remorse and sadness?

_____

_____

3) Joanna was fired for being in a fight at work. The other woman hit her with a heavy purse, and Joanna hadn't even hit back. Her boss wouldn't listen to her or her witnesses. How can she communicate the true story?

_____

_____

4) Anna is very attracted to Charlene, but is not sure if Charlene has noticed her at all. How can Anna communicate her feelings to her in a way in which she won't look stupid in case Charlene's not interested?

_____

_____

5) Alberta is very shy. She meets a very proper young man from Mexico at her cousin's wedding and dances with him. He offers to drive her home, and she accepts. She wants to kiss him, but is not sure that he wants to. She is too embarrassed to say anything. How could she communicate what she wants and find out what he wants without coming out and asking him to kiss her?

_____

_____

6) Roberta is starting a new job. She wants to look confident and like she knows what she is doing. What body language would give that message?

_____

_____

7) Louisa is feeling very frustrated. She doesn't feel she can talk to any of the people she shares an apartment with. She is not good at expressing herself in writing. How else can she let her feelings out?

_____

_____

8) Jenny meets Bob at an AA meeting. He is clearly interested in starting a relationship with her, but she doesn't want to get romantically involved because she doesn't have six months of sobriety. How can she let him know she isn't interested in a relationship now without hurting his feelings?

_____

_____

You can see that communications that hurt you or someone else are unhealthy. Usually, not communicating at all is unhealthy, too. Communicating to the wrong person is even more unhealthy because it puts you in a dangerous situation where you might reoffend. So, it is just as important to consider the consequences of your communications as it is to think about the consequences of the choices you make.

The second part of the exercise shows you that there are many different ways you can express your thoughts and feelings. In many of these situations, the person needed to assert herself.

Assertiveness is often misunderstood. People mix up assertiveness with aggressiveness or anger. When you yell at someone in anger, you are not being assertive. *Assertiveness is when you can make your needs, thoughts, or feelings known in a calm, convincing manner.*

For example, Georgia is trying to complete some work at home. Her husband keeps coming into her study and interrupting her. If she yells, "Get the hell out of here," she is not being assertive, she is being aggressive because she sounds threatening and out of control. To be assertive, she would say, "Please leave my room. I have to get this work done tonight." And if her husband doesn't get out, she would repeat firmly, "I need you to leave the room and stop interrupting me." She might even have to say it several times until she is heard.

One of the best ways to be assertive is to say what you are feeling rather than to criticize someone else. Sometimes people refer to this method as making "I-statements." For example, if you don't like the way your husband or partner is hanging on to your arm, it would be more assertive and effective to say, "I feel uncomfortable with the way you are holding my arm, please let go," rather than "You're always so possessive. Why do you always have to hang on to me?"

You can determine what is assertive and what is aggressive by the way you are feeling when you make certain statements and by the consequences. If you say something loudly and angrily or in a threatening way, you are most likely being aggressive. If you speak calmly and firmly, you are being assertive. The next exercise is a short one to help you distinguish between assertiveness and aggressiveness.

Exercise 61. Assertiveness vs. Aggressiveness

1) After each of the following statements circle whether the statement was aggressive or assertive.

a) Joan's eight-year-old daughter has gotten into her make-up drawer. Joan yells, "Get the &*^# out of here or I'll beat your ass." Aggressive or assertive?

b) When a friend grabs Barbara's letter from her boyfriend, Barbara says strongly, "Give me that letter back immediately." Aggressive or assertive?

c) When the friend starts to read it, Barbara repeats, "Give me the letter back immediately," and adds "if you want to stay friends." Aggressive or assertive?

d) When Elena wants Alexander to stop touching her breasts, she says firmly, "I want you to stop touching me right now." Aggressive or assertive?

e) When Alex doesn't stop, Elena repeats what she said and adds, "If you don't, I will never go out with you again. I mean it." Aggressive or assertive?

f) When he still doesn't stop, Elena adds, "If you don't stop, I will file a criminal complaint against you." Aggressive or assertive?

g) If Elena had said instead, "You son-of-a-bitch, you think you're God's gift to women. Well, you're nothing but a two-bit punk, and I'm going to make sure you get locked up for this!" Aggressive or assertive?

h) Belle's roommate messed up their room looking for an old shirt in Belle's dresser. Belle yells, "You jerk! You messed up all my stuff. Keep your mitts out of my drawers!" Aggressive or assertive?

i) Carla wants her boyfriend to turn down the TV so she can read. She asks him nicely, but he doesn't respond, so she yells, "Are you deaf? Turn down the damn TV!" Aggressive or assertive?

j) When Emma finds out her friend has brought drugs into her (Emma's) car, Emma says, "I'm afraid I can't drive you anywhere any more because you put my license in jeopardy by breaking my rules and the law, making me an accessory." Assertive or aggressive?

k) If Emma had said instead, "You stupid jerk, don't you ever listen to anyone? You know the rules, now get the hell out of my car!" Assertive or aggressive?

2) Now think of a time when you said something aggressively to someone. Describe the situation and write down what you said.

Situation:

_____

_____

What you said:

_____

_____

What is an assertive statement you could have made instead?

_____

_____

After making your assertive statement, if you don't get the response you want, it is important to make the same statement again even more strongly. Always look at what you are trying to accomplish with your statement. Do your best not to hurt the person's feelings. Even people who act obnoxiously have feelings. Often, they may feel really bad about themselves and cover the feelings up by acting badly. Can you think of anyone like that? Most of us know someone.

Telling someone what you want or would like to have happen is often more difficult than criticizing the actions of someone else. A positive example of assertiveness would be when one of your friends asks another of your friends to go to the show on Saturday. You would like to go, too. You have a choice to assert yourself or not. If you don't say what you want, you certainly won't get to go with them. If you whine, "You never ask me to do anything," instead of asserting yourself, you are likely to be misunderstood and disliked. But if you say, "May I join you?" you have positively asserted yourself.

While you might face the possibility of rejection by asking in an appropriately assertive manner, it is worth the chance. Even if you are told no, you have other options, such as asking other friends to go, going by yourself, doing some other activity, or going to visit your family instead. The rejection may have nothing to do with their liking or disliking you. Use your positive self-talk.

Telling someone what you don't want is also difficult, particularly if you are not sure what is going on with the other person. This is what happens in many child-molestation cases. The child victim may feel sort of funny—not sure if what the more powerful adult wants is okay or not. The victim often doesn't say no because he/she is afraid of offending the more powerful person, who is usually someone the victim likes or respects.

It is important to say what you feel and best to say it directly to the person involved (unless that puts your life in danger). There is almost always some risk, although it is usually small. Some people don't like it or feel threatened when others say what they are feeling or refuse to go along, but most others will respect you for standing up for yourself. It is most important, however, to recognize that when you assertively say what you really feel and make your own positive, healthy choices, you will feel good about yourself and respect yourself.

Communicating in healthy ways and being assertive takes practice. It's not easy, and you don't always get what you want even when you make clear, calm, assertive statements. But the more clearly you communicate, the more likely it is that you'll feel better about yourself and maybe even get what you're asking for.

It is okay to say no when you don't want to do something. You will feel better afterward. Lorna, who is being pressured to take drugs, could say, "Count me out. It's not my thing," or "Half my family are addicts and alcoholics. I don't want to end up like them." Maybe her friends would just say, "Okay, but you don't know what you're missing," and still think she was okay.

1) Think of a time when you said yes when you really meant no. Write down the situation, how you felt at the time, and how you felt afterward.

Situation:

_____

_____

How you felt at the time you said yes:

_____

_____

How you felt afterward:

_____

_____

2) Think of a time you said no when you really wanted to say yes.

Situation:

_____

_____

What kept you from expressing what you really meant?

_____

_____

3) List three situations in which you would like to say no, but have difficulty with it. Tell why.

a) Situation:

_____

_____

Reason:

_____

b) Situation:

_____

_____

Reason:

_____

c) Situation:

_____

_____

Reason:

_____

4) Can you think of a situation now where you are afraid to say yes when you really want to?

_____

_____

5) Why will you feel better about yourself when you say what you really mean and want?

_____

_____

6) Tell what you would say and what reason you would give to say yes or no in the following situations:

a) You are best friends with Marcia who is divorcing. She asks you to help her hide marital assets. You don't want to. How would you tell her no? Explain your reasoning to her in the answer.

_____

_____

_____

b) Pete, your best friend, asks to borrow money from you. You don't have any to spare, and, besides, he never paid you back for the last loan you gave him. How do you tell him no?

_____

_____

c) Your boss asks you to stay late at work for the third time in a week. Your spouse will be furious if you stay late again, but also you are worried that your boss will fire you if you don't. How can you say no to your boss?

_____

_____

d) Your best friend asks you out to dinner at a very elegant restaurant. You would like to go, but are afraid you will feel uncomfortable. How can you say yes, but let your friend know your fears?

_____

_____

e) Make up a scene from your own life where you could have asserted yourself by saying no or yes and act it out with another person.

_____

_____

_____

_____

_____

People communicate nonverbally, that is, without words. Have you ever known that your husband or partner was feeling fed-up and angry before he/she ever said a word? Or that a good friend was overjoyed about something before he/she ever said anything? Have you ever smashed a wall with your fist to get your anger out? These are all examples of nonverbal communication.

Every now and then someone's body language or facial expression is out of step with what is going on. For example, Shawn's dog died and Shawn smiled while talking about it. Sometimes people who have closed off their emotions, including many people who have been abused, act this way.

Sometimes children smile or laugh when they are being scolded by a parent or teacher. Usually it is not because they think it is funny, but because they're nervous or would rather laugh than let anyone know they're upset enough to cry. Often adults don't understand and punish a child because they think the child is showing disrespect or not taking the situation seriously. This can happen with adults, too. Has this ever happened to you?

If you can, and if it doesn't put you in physical danger, it is better to allow yourself to show with your body and face exactly what you are feeling. People relate more completely to people who communicate in body language as well as words.

Some fun exercises you can do in group to practice nonverbal communication are called Communication Charades.

Exercise 63. Communication Charades

1) Write the following messages on separate pieces of paper. Have each person pick a message without letting anyone else see it. Have one person at a time act out her message without using words. Keep a record of the time it takes the others to guess what emotion that person is trying to communicate.

a) Leave me alone.

b) I want to make love to you.

c) Go away.

d) Come here.

e) Stop that.

f) Please take me with you.

g) Don't hurt me.

h) What time is it?

i) Let's play.

j) I have work to do.

Think up additional messages of your own, too.

_____

_____

_____

_____

_____

If someone smiles and looks happy when she says, "My cat died last night," you will understand that the cat died by the words she says, but be confused by her facial expression and body language. It is important that you are authentic in how you show what you are feeling, expressing your emotions in your voice and body as well as your words. This shows that you are in touch with your feelings. And if you are in touch with your own feelings, it is easier for you to make the link to what others are feeling.

Did anyone ever say to you, "You're not really sorry"? If so, were you sorry? Or were you just faking it because you didn't want to accept the consequences? If you really were sorry, you probably didn't communicate it very well.

Think about something you really regretted doing when you were a child. Try saying the words, "I am very sorry," while you think about your regret. Express your sorrow in your face and body. Then, think of a time you said, "I'm sorry," when you weren't sorry at all; you were just saying it because you thought you had to. Show how you feel this time in your facial expression and how you hold your body. If you are really doing this well, people should be able to tell how you are feeling as well as hear what you are saying. Try this out in group or with your friends. Ask them how well you did.

After all the work you have done on emotions, empathy, and communication, you are now in better touch with your feelings and communicating them both verbally and nonverbally. You're likely a better "sender." This leads us into the next portion of our communication chapter: receiving the message. For every thought or feeling to be communicated, there must be someone who is listening to or observing it. Perception (listening/observing) is just as important as sending. It is also the part that most people practice least. It is particularly important for you, as a sex offender, to be very aware of what others are communicating, especially potential victims. If you had really been aware of what your victim was trying to communicate to you, either in words or body language, you might have chosen not to offend or participate in an offense.

Often, women just beginning treatment have difficulty really listening to what others say. This may be because they need attention and/or have not learned to listen well, or their own needs interfere. They hear what they want to hear because their needs are more important than anyone else's. Does this describe you? It is extremely important to our communication and relationships with others to make an effort to really listen. It is equally important to read other people's body language and facial expressions. The next exercise will help you do that.

Exercise 64. Listening & Observing

1) Candy babysat her favorite nephew, Paul, who was ten. He showed that he really liked her by always asking his mother to have her babysit and by hugging her when she came over. He would offer to give her back rubs, and she would give him back rubs as well. She felt sexually attracted to him. She began to rub his buttocks, as well as his back. He didn't say anything, but squirmed away from her.

What message was he probably trying to give her?

_____

_____

Why do you think he didn't just say to her, "Don't rub my butt"?

_____

_____

2) Mary Jo started to sexually fondle her sleeping daughter. She didn't think the child was aware of it because her daughter seemed to be asleep. Each time she would begin to do it, however, the child would roll over, away from her.

Do you think the child was really asleep or pretending to be asleep?

_____

If she was pretending, what do you think that Mary Jo's daughter was trying to communicate to her mother?

_____

_____

Why would she pretend instead of saying something?

_____

_____

The days after Mary Jo would molest her, her daughter seemed to misbehave more than usual. Might she be communicating something? _____

What might that be?

_____

_____

3) Gloria and her co-worker, Ali, liked each other and became good friends. When they were talking one day, Gloria told Ali that she was a lesbian. Ali said that she was, too. Gloria invited Ali to her home where they started to have sex. Gloria's partner came in and Gloria invited her to join in a threesome with them. Ali was very uncomfortable with this, since she only had sex before with someone she knew, cared about and felt intimate with. But she didn't say anything.

Why do you think she didn't say anything?

_____

_____

If she wouldn't look at Gloria the next day at work, what was she possibly communicating?

_____

_____

4) Did your victim say no to you? _____

If so, did you listen and stop? _____

Were you aware of your victim's body language? _____

What was it?

_____

_____

If your victim was communicating "no" through body language, why didn't you stop?

_____

_____

Do you remember what expression was on your victim's face when you were sexually abusing him/her? _____

Describe it.

_____

What about your victim's body language? Did the victim turn or pull away, look frozen, cry, or hunch over in fear?)

_____

Picture your victim in your mind. Draw a picture of your victim's face below. Show what you think your victim's main emotion was.

When we listen, we receive information on two levels: the thought level and the feeling level. For example, Jean's boyfriend invites her to a rock concert. She loves him, but she hates heavy-metal music. She might say, "I would be glad to go with you," meaning she is willing to go, but underneath he can sense that on the feeling level, she doesn't really want to go. Or you ask your husband if your brother and his family can stay with you while they are looking for an apartment. He can't stand your brother, but he says "sure" anyway. But you recognize that underneath, on the feeling level, he will hate having them there.

To understand what people are saying and what they are feeling when they transmit a message to you, it is necessary to watch body language, hear vocal inflections, and notice facial expressions, as well as listening to the words a person is saying. Just as healthy expressive communication requires that you use good verbal and nonverbal skills, reception or listening requires that you use your eyes, as well as your ears.

Do the next exercise in group or with a partner. It will give you an opportunity to express yourself in words and body language and to receive messages both on the thought and feeling levels.

Exercise 65. Giving & Receiving Communications

Part 1: Thought level

In group, pair up, then tell the other person all about one of the most exciting things that ever happened to you—when it happened, where you were, who was there, what happened, and why you were so excited. When you finish, have the person repeat the facts back to you. Did the person fully understand what you said? Correct any differences or misconceptions. Then trade roles so the other person tells you all about one of the most exciting things that ever happened to her.

You can also do this exercise in a circle, where you tell the person next to you, who tells the person next to her what you said, then that person tells the person next to her what you said, and so on, until the last person tells you. You then tell the last person how accurate the final recounting is and correct the differences. The group also figures out where the story changed. This is a variation on the children's game where you whisper something into the first person's ear, and so on.

Try this exercise with other life experiences, like the most important day of your life, the most embarrassing thing that ever happened to you, and so forth.

Part 2: Feeling level

This exercise is similar to the last, but the emotional content is not known in advance. There are two sections to this part.

1) Tell another person about a significant experience you had as a child. Tell your-self in your head what you were feeling about this experience, but don't tell the other person out loud in words. As you talk about the time, place, people involved, and what happened, let your feelings be known through your vocal inflection, facial expression, and body language. Do not exaggerate. When you finish, the person will tell you the basic facts of the story and what it appeared that you were feeling at the time. Discuss how accurate the person was regarding both the thought and feeling content of the story.

Also do this exercise with other happenings where you felt some strong emo-tions—with family, love and/or sexual experiences, job situations, and so forth.

2) In this part of the exercise you can either break up into pairs or do it as though you were playing charades in a group. Say each of the following phrases in a way that expresses one of the feelings written after it. The other person or group must guess which of the feelings you are expressing.

"I'm furious."—joking, upset, sarcastic

"I love you."—loving, hateful, teasing

"You stink."—joking, unacceptable, angry

"I'm sorry."—sincere, angry, afraid

"I feel sick."—disgusted, unwell, bored

"I'm lost."—frightened, angry, sarcastic

"I'll miss you."—sad, flirtatious, angry

"My name is…"—friendly, angry, flirtatious

"Who are you?"—curious, threatening, afraid

"What do you want?"—nervous, curious, angry

"I don't understand."—confused, hurt, angry

"I'm through."—confident, disgusted, sad

"You're cute."—sexy, admiring, disgusted

"You goofed."—angry, laughing, weary

"I'm afraid."—terrified, sarcastic, worried

Make up additional phrases of your own and different ways to express them.

Often, people think they are listening to others, but they are really too into themselves to pick up the message and emotional content. This is especially true of parents with their children, when the parents have a lot of things on their minds. It is also true of spouses, who often think they know what their partner is going to say and just blow them off. And it is true of women who molest children; they don't absorb the body language, the words that are said or not said, and/or the feelings the child is subtly projecting.

This week try to really listen to what people are saying to you. Check out the content and feelings behind the statements by repeating them back to the person. For example, if a good friend says to you, "I'm so mad at my son I could kill him. He got kicked out of school for fighting again." What is she really telling you and why? She is most likely not saying she will really kill her son, so mirror back what you think she means by saying something like, "You really sound frustrated with your son's behavior." Try it. You'll find out how good you are at really listening, and those around you will appreciate your understanding if you listen well.

The best way to learn to express yourself and receive communications from others is to use various types of communication. This means practicing good communication not just this week, but all the time. Practice at home, at work, everywhere you go. Say what you are thinking and feeling and listen to and watch what other people are trying to say to you.

Good communication is necessary for all types of relationships. It is critical to your success in love relationships, in work settings, at school, at home, in recreational situations, and so forth.

Summary

You had the opportunity to learn about the following aspects of communication:

1) That communication includes both verbal and nonverbal expression.

2) That communication can be both direct and indirect.

3) How to distinguish between healthy and unhealthy communication.

4) More ways of communicating in a healthy manner.

5) The difference between assertiveness and aggressiveness.

6) How to be assertive and say what you mean.

7) The importance of your facial expressions and body language in showing what you mean.

8) The importance of listening well (reception).

9) Awareness of listening on both the thought and feeling levels.

10) The importance of practicing communication skills in everyday life.

Chapter 21

Ending Thoughts

Congratulations! By the time you get to this chapter, you will have completed the readings and exercises, discussed them with your therapist and group, and be well on your way to completing your therapy requirement and embarking on your new life of better choices. Now you are ready to put all you have learned into practice. You are ready to lead a healthier, happier lifestyle, one where you can stand on your own two feet, make healthy and informed choices, have more successful relationships, better communicate your needs, understand what others are communicating to you, and never get yourself in a situation where offending would be an option.

We hope you can apply what you have learned to all aspects of your life, not just offending. Remember, you have to weave what you have learned into your everyday life, using the various techniques on a regular basis.

It would be beneficial for you to periodically reread this book and your responses to the exercises. And even when you have officially completed therapy, it's good to come back and process problems that are bothering you with your therapist and have periodic refresher sessions. We all tend to fall back into old, dysfunctional ways of behaving when left to our own devices. Old habits are hard to break. Continuing to practice what you have learned, getting periodic help, and reminding yourself not to use the old non-functional coping strategies, can help you live that happier, more fulfilling, crime-free life.

Especially remember that you always have choices about what you do and think. And there are usually many of them. You have the power to make decisions with either positive or negative consequences for yourself and for others. Push yourself into making healthy, satisfying, non-damaging choices by analyzing the possible results of these choices. (Sometimes, however, your choice may have to be the one that is least damaging, or the least painful for a child.) Decide which ones will afford you the best results. Avoid and escape from the negative or dangerous ones.

When you lapse—and you will, nearly everyone does, although with more practice lapses become less and less common—don't give up. Get out of the situation before you re-offend.

You can succeed. You can create a better, offense-free life for yourself. Just keep reminding yourself that success is a lifelong process. You have to keep working at it—working at preventing relapse relative to your offenses and working at your relationships, your attitudes toward self and others, your ability to communicate and assert yourself, your self-destructive or destructive-to-others behaviors, and everything else.

Just to make sure you understand what you've read, the following is a quiz on these concepts. See how well you do. Review your responses with your therapist. If you do poorly, go back and and reread the items you have forgotten.

Exercise 66. Final Quiz

Answer the following questions with True or False.

1) You can choose your behavior but not the consequences. _____

2) Women who commit sex offenses can't change their behavior. _____

3) Women who have worked through their own victimizations are less likely to reoffend. _____

4) Relapse prevention teaches you how to prevent reoffense by breaking down the steps in offending into small manageable pieces. _____

5) The offense cycle shows you how your offending pattern can be repeated over and over. _____

6) When you get to the "giving up" stage of your offense chain, it is too late to prevent reoffense. _____

7) Children will tell you if they don't want to participate in sexual activities. _____

8) Sex and intimacy are the same thing. _____

9) Every choice you make has both good and bad consequences. _____

10) In a good relationship, the woman should always be there sexually for the man. _____

11) Autonomy means looking out only for yourself. _____

12) A codependent relationship is one in which you help your partner. _____

13) Assertiveness is making your needs known without getting angry. _____

14) Empathy means stepping into another person's shoes, understanding what they are feeling. _____

15) It is better if you don't ever let yourself feel your painful emotions. _____

16) A woman isn't complete without a partner. _____

17) If a teenage boy enjoyed having sex with an adult woman, no sexual abuse occurred. _____

18) Cutting on yourself is a dysfunctional way of handling your own emotions. _____

19) It is unhealthy not to have sex if you have a sexual urge. _____

20) It's not sexual abuse if you don't touch the other person. _____

21) Women shouldn't have sexual urges. _____

22) Suicidal behavior usually occurs as the result of dysfunctional coping with painful emotions. _____

Now answer the following items in full.

1) Think of something you want to do. What are the positive and negative consequences of doing it?

Positive: _____

_____

Negative: _____

_____

What are the positive and negative consequences of not doing it?

Positive: _____

_____

Negative: _____

_____

2) What needs did you satisfy when you made the choice to commit or participate in a sex offense?

_____

_____

List two healthier ways you could have satisfied each of those needs.

_____

_____

_____

_____

3) Make a relapse-prevention offense chain for yourself below. Next to each item, list what you could have said to yourself and what you could have done instead.

SUD: _____

   Said: _____

   Done: _____

Risky Situation: _____

   Said: _____

   Done: _____

Lapse: _____

   Said: _____

   Done: _____

AVE/Giving Up: _____

   Said: _____

   Done: _____

4) What was going on in your life that put you on the path to sex offending or participating in a sex offense?

_____

_____

What could you do differently now that would change that situation?

_____

_____

5) List three risk factors that would cause you to reoffend.

_____

_____

_____

What usually triggers them?

_____

_____

What are some things you can do to diffuse or lessen your risk factors?

_____

_____

_____

6) List three types of each of the following kinds of abuse.

Physical abuse:

_____

_____

_____

Sexual abuse:

_____

_____

_____

Emotional abuse:

_____

_____

_____

Circle each of the above that you suffered. (If you never suffered any of these, write down something that made you feel bad.)

_____

List at least three ways the abuse (or whatever made you feel bad) made you feel.

_____

_____

_____

List at least three ways your victim(s) might have felt.

_____

_____

_____

7) List three or more ways or times you have violated another person's boundaries.

_____

_____

_____

_____

8) Describe how a healthy relationship should develop. What are the steps?

_____

_____

_____

9) Describe what a healthy sexual relationship should be like.

_____

_____

_____

10) Describe what *autonomy* means.

_____

_____

_____

11) What is the difference between being alone and being lonely?

_____

_____

_____

12) Write down a self-destructive behavior you have engaged in.

_____

_____

What are some ways you can prevent yourself from doing this in the future?

_____

_____

_____

13) Give an example of both a verbal and a nonverbal way of expressing the same thing. What is the person trying to communicate?

_____

_____

Verbal statement:

_____

_____

Nonverbal expression:

_____

_____

14) What is the difference between aggressiveness and assertiveness?

_____

_____

_____

Give an example of each.

Aggressive statement:

_____

_____

Assertive statement:

_____

_____

15) What feelings were you communicating when you committed or participated in your sex offense(s)?

_____

_____

How could you better communicate those feelings (list at least three ways)?

_____

_____

_____

16) What was the most important thing you learned from this workbook?

_____

_____

_____

Why?

_____

_____

_____

Remember that even when you have completed or "graduated" from your required treatment, you will still have to consciously and regularly practice what you have learned, so that you will continue to lead a satisfying and healthy life. What you have learned here is an ongoing process. Good luck in maintaining your gains.

Glossary

abstinence: Staying free from sex offending behaviors.

Abstinence Violation Effect (AVE): The point in the relapse chain where you give up; you feel you are already a failure and think only of the positive aspects of the abusive behavior.

abuser: Someone who does an act that is harmful to another person.

adaptive coping response: A change in thoughts, feelings, and/or behaviors that helps you deal with risk factors in a healthy way, reducing the risk of reoffense.

assault cycle: The pattern of thoughts, feelings, and behaviors that leads up to and follows your sexually offending behavior.

autonomy: Not subject to the rule or control of someone else—independent, self-sufficient, and self-directing.

aversive conditioning: A technique to reduce deviant sexual arousal by pairing unpleasant stimuli (like ammonia or rotten food) with the arousal.

castration: Removal of the testicles in men and the ovaries in women.

chemical castration: Use of medications to suppress the production of male hormones.

child pornography: Any audio, visual, or written material that portrays children engaging in any type of sexual behavior or that depicts children's genitalia for other than scientific/medical reasons.

clarification: A treatment technique where you write a letter to the victim taking full responsibility for the sexual abuse, clarifying what happened and describing what you are doing to prevent yourself from offending again.

codependence: When a person gives up his/her identity, desires, and dreams, often with resentment.

cognitive distortion: Thinking errors, including excuses for, justifications for, and minimizations of the sex offending behaviors.

cognitive restructuring: A treatment method where you learn healthy thinking methods and understand your prior distorted thinking and unhealthy attitudes.

contact: Written, verbal, or physical contact—in person, from afar, or by communication through a third party—with another person. Many offenders have no-contact orders with their victims (and other minors if they abused a child). Usually these orders specify what, if any, contact is allowed.

covert sensitization: A technique to reduce deviant sexual arousal by pairing a deviant fantasy with an unpleasant one.

denial: A sex offender's way of saving face by not admitting all or part of his abusive behavior or minimizing some aspects of it.

detumescence: When a fully or partially erect penis becomes soft, resulting from drainage of blood from the penis tissue, usually occurring because the man is no longer aroused.

deviant arousal: Sexual arousal from abusive or unusual sexual stimuli, including children, exposure, violence, peeping, obscene phone calls, etc.

disinhibitors: Stimuli (such as alcohol, child pornography, etc.) that decrease your conscience or ability to stop yourself from committing a sexually abusive act or the steps leading to one.

empathy: Awareness of the feelings and ideas of another person.

family reunification: A step-by-step process to put the family unit together again, which is based on safety, treatment progress of the abuser, and readiness of the victim.

graduation or discharge readiness: The point in your treatment when you have accomplished the treatment goals, have decreased your risk of sexual reoffense, have put your relapse prevention plans in place, and have adequately practiced.

high-risk factors: Inside or outside events or feelings that threaten your sense of control and increase your risk of lapsing or sexually reoffending.

incest: Sexual behaviors between close relatives, like parent and child, step-child, partner's child, nieces, or nephews.

justification: A thinking error where an abuser makes excuses for his sex-offending behavior.

lapse: An urge, fantasy, or thought about sexually abusing or an act that comes dangerously close to an offense.

lesbian: A homosexual woman; a woman who prefers sex with another woman.

level of risk: The degree of dangerousness of a sex offender, rated by use of risk assessment instruments and factors correlating to high and low risk that are present in an offender.

maladaptive coping response: An unhealthy way of dealing with a risk factor. These responses place an offender closer to reoffense/relapse.

masturbation: Touching or rubbing or penetrating your own body for sexual gratification.

minimization: An offender's attempt to decrease or downplay his/her offending behavior—the extent of it, its effect on the victim, etc. This is usually a thinking error on his/her part.

obscene: A legal finding that some sexual material is so horrible that it is not acceptable. This is an exception to the free speech protection of the First Amendment of the Constitution.

obsession: Where an offender has constantly recurring thoughts about a person, object, or idea, which he feels unable to shake from his mind.

offense chain (or reoffense chain): The various events that precede and lead to sexual (re)offending.

offense cycle: The pattern of thoughts, feelings, and behaviors that lead up to and follow your sexually offending behavior.

oral copulation: The act of using a mouth on the sexual organs for arousal.

orgasmic reconditioning: A behavioral technique to reduce inappropriate sexual arousal.

overdependence: When a person is overly reliant on another person or persons to get his/her needs met.

paraphilia: A disorder of sexual behavior, where a person has recurrent thoughts, fantasies, urges, or behaviors that are either illegal or cause him/her problems in functioning.

pedophile: A person who has recurrent sexual thoughts, fantasies, urges, or behaviors toward children.

phallometry (phallometric assessment or penile plethysmography): Measurement of sexual arousal levels by use of an electronic instrument.

plethysmograph: An electronic instrument that measures sexual arousal levels.

polygraph: An electronic instrument that measures truth telling vs. falsehoods.

pornography: Writing, photographs, art, motion pictures, or other forms of expression, whose main purpose is sexual arousal. (Child pornography is where children are the subjects. It is illegal.)

positive treatment outcome: An offender's risk of sexual reoffense is significantly reduced.

precocious sexuality: Premature (overly early) sexual interest and sexual behaviors in children.

precursors: All of the events or factors that precede and lead to a sex offense. These include all of the elements of your offense chain and your cycle of offense.

Problem of Immediate Gratification (PIG): A part of the AVE (Abstinence Violation Effect/ Giving Up) stage, in which you focus only on your urges and the good sensations you will feel satisfying them, and you forget the later negative effects.

programmed coping responses: Healthy reactions to stressors or risk factors that are so well practiced, they become automatic.

progress in treatment: Measurement of how well you are learning and practicing all the techniques and lifestyle changes necessary to prevent yourself from reoffending.

promiscuous: Having sexual contact with many persons.

psychotropic medications: Medicines that help a person's mental state.

puberty: The stage in life when a child's reproductive organs begin to work and the adult sexual characteristics develop (genital hair, breast development, etc.)

rape: A legal term for forcible penetration usually of the vagina, but in some jurisdictions of other body openings as well.

recidivism: Reoffense.

relapse: A reocurring sexually abusive behavior or sex offense.

relapse prevention: A multi-faceted model using cognitive and behavioral techniques to treat sex offenders, with the goal of reducing reoffense/relapse.

release of information: A document you sign to allow the sharing of information about you between the people listed on the release.

risk factor: A painful emotion or thought that places an offender in a position where he/she is more likely to commit or participate in a sex offense.

risky situation: The step on the relapse chain during which you place yourself in a dangerous position where you are capable of reoffending.

sadism: Getting sexually aroused by hurting someone physically or mentally.

Seemingly Unimportant Decisions (SUDs): Decisions that seem reasonable on the surface, but place you in a risky situation where you have the opportunity or greater likelihood to reoffend.

Selective Serotonin Reuptake Inhibitors (SSRIs): Antidepressants that are often used to help control deviant sexual urges and fantasies.

self-actualization: Becoming the person you want to be (as much as you are able).

self-deprecation: Putting yourself down.

sex offender: Any person who has committed or participated in an illegal sexual act, whether or not charged or convicted.

sex offender registration: Laws requiring you to register your address and other identifying information with law enforcement or other designated state agencies. (Make sure to know the laws of your state.)

sexual abuse cycle: The pattern of thoughts, feelings, and behaviors that lead up to and follow your sexually offending behavior.

sexual abuser: Any person who has committed an illegal sexual act, whether or not charged or convicted.

sexual assault: Any forced, manipulated, or unwanted sexual contact between you and another person.

sexual contact: Any sexual act, physical or visual, with another person's genitals, breasts, and/or mouths, or other behaviors of a sexual nature.

sexual deviancy: Any sexual thoughts or behaviors that are illegal or abnormal.

sexual predator: A dangerous sex offender, usually one suffering from a mental disorder increasing his likelihood of sexual reoffense.

sodomy: The sexual penetration of the anal cavity (asshole) with an object or bodily part.

successful completion of treatment: See **graduation**.

suppression: Pushing down (stuffing) thoughts and feelings rather than working on them. Offenders who suppress their thoughts and feelings are more likely to cope poorly and dangerously.

thinking error: See **cognitive distortion**.

treatment program: An inpatient or outpatient place where sex offenders are treated.

treatment progress: See **progress in treatment**.

trigger: An event that could activate risk factors leading to sexual reoffending.

victim stance: A thinking error in which you consider yourself to be more a victim of your offense than the actual victim.

Recommended Reading

Bass, E. and L. Davis. *The Courage to Heal: A Guide for Women Survivors of Child Sexual Abuse.* New York: Harper and Row, 1988.

Bear, E. and P. Dimock. *Adults Molested As Children: A Survivor's Manual for Women and Men.* Brandon, VT: The Safer Society Press, 1988.

Davin, P., T. Dunbar, and J. Hislop. *Female Sexual Abusers: Three Views.* Brandon, VT: The Safer Society Press, 1999.

Davis, L. *The Courage to Heal Workbook.* New York: Harper and Row, 1990.

Eldridge, H. *Maintaining Change: A Personal Relapse Prevention Manual.* Thousand Oaks, CA: Sage Publications, 1998.

Gil, E. *Outgrowing the Pain: A Book for and about Adults Abused As Children.* Walnut Creek, CA: Launch Press, 1988.

Gorski, T. T. *The Staying Sober Workbook.* Independence, MO: Independence Press, 1988.

Herrington, R. L. *The Cognitive Therapy Workbook.* San Diego, CA: CTR, 1987.

Johnson, S. A. *Man-to-Man: When Your Partner Says No.* Brandon, VT: The Safer Society Press, 1988.

Matthews, R., J. K. Matthews, and K. Speltz. *Female Sex Offenders.* Brandon, VT: The Safer Society Press, 1989.

Mayer, A. *Women Sex Offenders.* Holmes Beach, FL: Learning Publications, Inc., 1992.

Miletski, H. *Mother-Son Incest: The Unthinkable Broken Taboo.* Brandon, VT: The Safer Society Press, 1995.

Robinson, S. L. *Growing Beyond: A Workbook for Teenage Girls.* Holyoke, MA: NEARI Press, 2002.

Rosencrans, B. *The Last Secret: Daughters Sexually Abused by Mothers.* Brandon, VT: The Safer Society Press, 1997.

Schwartz, B. K. and G. M. S. Canfield. *Facing the Shadow.* Kingston, NJ: Civic Research Institute, Inc., 1996.

Sonkin, D. J. and M. Durphy. *Learning to Live Without Violence: A Handbook for Men.* Volcano, CA: Volcano Press, 1989.

Steen, C. *The Adult Relapse Prevention Workbook.* Brandon, VT: The Safer Society Press, 2001.

Terry, J. M. *The Workbook for Sex Offenders.* Jacksonville, AR: Jax House Publications, 1992.

Turner, M. T. and T. N. Turner. *Female Adolescent Sexual Abusers: An Exploratory Study of Mother-Daughter Dynamics with Implications for Treatment,* Brandon, VT: The Safer Society Press, 1994.

Yokley, J. M. (ed.). *The Use of Victim-Offender Communication in the Treatment of Sexual Abuse.* Brandon, VT: The Safer Society Press, 1990.

Notes

Selected Titles from Safer Society Press
Resources for Families

Outside Looking In
When Someone You Love Is in Therapy
Author: Patrice Moulton, Ph.D. and Lin Harper, Ph.D.

Families and friends may sigh with relief when their troubled loved ones finally get help through therapy. But then what? The changes in mood, attention, and behavior that may accompany therapeutic intervention are likely to evoke mixed reactions in what has been until now a neglected population: the client's support community of family and friends.

They may feel afraid or anxious or out of the loop and out of control. They may express these feelings in ways that create unnecessary challenges to the therapeutic process and the progress of the client. *Outside Looking In* can help by providing a guide to the therapeutic process and practical survival tips for the client's family members and loved ones.

In clear language and with a minimum of jargon Moulton and Harper explain the counseling process, including confidentiality, and its typical stages. The stories they share are adapted from real counseling situations, and the exercises they've included at the end of each chapter help readers understand their own reactions and feelings.

ISBN-13: 978-1-884444-57-9 · ISBN-10: 1-884444-57-1 · 144 pages, paper · $20.00 · Order#: WP072

What's Happening In Our Family
Understanding Sexual Abuse through Metaphors
Connie Ostis, Ph.D., L.C.S.W.

In her book *What's Happening in Our Family? Understanding Sexual Abuse Through Metaphors*, author Connie Ostis, helps adults - parents, educators, counselors - understand how abuse occurs by using stories that expose the manipulative relationships established and maintained by abusers.

The metaphors explain how sexual abuse begins in hidden ways and deepens in secrecy; clarify what harm is caused and how long it lasts; suggest how to cope with the "whirlpool" of emotions; help adults provide the support children need; and explain guidelines for keeping children safe. Using the non-threatening language of these stoires, adults can help children recognize when they are being manipulated and understand why they are not responsible for their abuse. (2002)

ISBN-13: 978-1-884444-65-4 · ISBN-10: 1-884444-65-2 · 212 pages, paper · $20.00 · Order#: WP089

When You Don't Know Who to Call
A Consumer's Guide to Selecting Mental Health Care
Nancy Schaufele, M.S.W., and Donna B. Kennedy

While the vast majority of people get the help they need from mental health professionals, people in desperate need may receive mediocre or even harmful "treatment" from therapists or inpatient treatment centers. Therapist Nancy Schaufele, M.S.W., and referral specialist Donna B. Kennedy combine years of private practice outpatient treatment, referral and inpatient evaluation experience. Drawing on real case histories, they show readers both how to qualify the help they are seeking and the warning signs of situations to avoid. Provides practical, easy-to-use guidelines and checklists for both outpatient and inpatient care. (1998)

ISBN-13: 978-1-884444-48-7 · ISBN-10: 1-884444-48-2 · 144 pages, paper · $15.00 · Order#: WP060

Resources for Professionals

Current Practices and Trends in Sexual Abuser Management
The Safer Society 2002 Nationwide Survey
Author: Robert J. McGrath, Georgia F. Cumming and Brenda L. Burchard

Safer Society's 2002 Nationwide Survey reports on the responses from more than 2,200 residential and community sexual abuser treatment programs for male and female adults, adolescents, and children. This report provides a wide-angle snapshot of the state of the field, and identifies trends in the assessment and treatment of sexual abusers. Both the current practices and trends are compared with what research and professional associations presently consider "best practice" in the field. Areas requiring additional research are identified and suggestions for program development and evaluation are included. This book provides invaluable information for practitioners, researchers, and policy makers. (2003)

ISBN-13: 978-1-884444-70-8 · ISBN-10: 1-884444-70-9 · 96 pages, paper · $22.00 · Order#: WP103

Female Adolescent Sexual Abusers
An Exploratory Study of Mother-Daughter Dynamics with Implications for Treatment
Marcia T. Turner, Psy.D. and Tracey N. Turner, M.A., A.D.T.R.

In this 70-page pilot study, Marcia and Tracey Turner describe their collaboration in the treatment of 8 adolescent female sexual abusers. The Turners see two powerful dynamics affecting their clients' tendency to act out through sexual abuse: clients' identification with the aggressors who had abused them; and the young women's relationships with mothers who had previously undisclosed sexual trauma in their own histories. (1994)

ISBN-13: 978-1-884444-16-6 · ISBN-10: 1-884444-16-4 · 70 pages, paper · $18.00 · Order#: WP027

Female Sexual Abusers
Three Views
Patricia Davin, Teresa Dunbar, & Julia Hislop

While a few more resources exist now than ten years ago, literature on female sexual abusers is still sparse. Female abuser typologies are in flux, motivations rely more on assumptions than research results, treatment modalities continue to be adapted from those used with men, and treatment outcomes remain undocumented.

In *Female Sexual Abusers: Three Views* Drs. Davin, Dunbar, and Hislop look at different aspects of female sexual abusers. Their rigorous, detailed research provides a deeper understanding of why women abuse. Beginning with extensive literature reviews, their examination of women who abuse ranges from the characteristics of co-offenders, to factors in the etiology of offending for women, to comparisons of psychosocial histories of women abusers and non-offending women in the same milieus.

Their fascinating findings challenge common beliefs and move our understanding forward by uncovering the secrets of this most hidden form of child sexual abuse. (1999)

ISBN-13: 978-1-884444-53-1 · ISBN-10: 1-884444-53-9 · 256 pages, paper · $22.00 · Order#: WP067

For more information about these titles, or any other **Safer Society Press** title, contact the Safer Society Foundation, at 802-247-3132 or visit the web site at www.safersociety.org.

Handbook of Sexual Abuser Assessment and Treatment, The
Edited by Mark Carich, Ph.D. & Steven E. Mussack, Ph.D.

Safer Society is pleased to publish this long-awaited compendium. With chapters from William Marshall, Robert McGrath, Emily Coleman, James Haaven, Alvin Lewis, Laren Bays, William Murphy, Peter Loss, Jerry Thomas, and Gary Lowe, as well as from the editors and others, this volume provides an essential basic outline of comprehensive treatment—the perfect introduction and reference volume that should be on every clinician's shelf. (2001)

ISBN-13: 978-1-884444-58-6 · ISBN-10: 1-884444-58-X · 272 pages, paper · $28.00 · Order#: WP083

The Last Secret
Daughters Sexually Abused by Mothers
Bobbie Rosencrans, M.S.W.

If you have looked for research on mothers as sexual abusers, and daughters of sexually abusive mothers you have discovered how little there is. Look no further. Bobbie Rosencrans' groundbreaking research will answer many of your questions and address a major gap in our understanding of these survivors and their mothers. Using the results of an extensive and detailed questionnaire sent to daughters sexually abused by their mothers, Bobbie Rosencrans has compiled a compelling portrait of both the effects of such abuse and the daughters' past and current relationships with their abusive mothers. Perhaps most apalling, few of the respondents had discussed their abuse even with their therapists. Abuse by mothers is clearly *The Last Secret*, a secret that these respondents and Bobbie Rosencrans are not willing to keep any more. (1997)

ISBN-13: 978-1-884444-36-4 · ISBN-10: 1-884444-36-9 · 261 pages, paper · $20.00 · Order#: WP046

Web of Meaning
A Developmental-Contextual Approach in Sexual Abuse Treatment
Gail Ryan and Associates

Why do some victims of sexual abuse sustain extreme trauma while others with similar experiences appear to emerge virtually unscathed? Why do some victims of sexual abuse become sexual abusers themselves? Many researcher and clinicians have sought to answer these questions by focusing on the nature and duration of the abuse. In *Web of Meaning*, Gail Ryan and her associates in the C. Henry Kempe Children's Center Study Group suggest a different approach. Meaningful treatment, they write, means developing therapeutic interventions specifically tailored to the individual rather than solely to the event. Based on a developmental perspective, *Web of Meaning* provides the reader with a matrix -- a tool designed to organize the process of searching for and putting together significant pieces of information about individual clients. The design of the matrix is based on the need to understand the larger picture of a client's life in order to make sense of what is currently being observed. A major goal of treatment, Ryan and Associates suggest, is rejection of victim or victimizer as an identity and self-regulation of lingering emotional and behavioral effects. (1999)

ISBN-13: 978-1-884444-50-0 · ISBN-10: 1-884444-50-4 · 192 pages, paper · $22.00 · Order#: WP065

For more information about these titles, or any other **Safer Society Press** title, contact the Safer Society Foundation, at 802-247-3132 or visit the web site at www.safersociety.org.

Order Form

PO Box 340, Brandon, VT 05733 • phone: 802-247-3132 • fax: 802-247-4233 • www.safersociety.org

Name		Date	
Agency			
Phone		Fax	
Shipping Address		Billing Address (if different)	

Title	Order#	Qty	Price	Total

Shipping & Handling Fee *subject to change without notice* (continental US only, others call)

☐ 1 book–$5   ☐ 1 video–$8   ☐ 2-4 items–$8   ☐ 5-10 items–$11
☐ 11-15 items–$15   ☐ 16-20 items–$17   ☐ 21-25 items–$20   ☐ 26-30 items–$23
☐ 31-35 items–$26   ☐ 36-40 items–$29   ☐ 41-50 items–$34   ☐ over 50 items–call

Shipping	
VT residents 6% tax	
Total	

Method of payment	☐ check ☐ money order ☐ Visa ☐ MC # ☐ purchase order (Gov't entities only)
Credit card or PO#	*exp. date*
Card holder's signature	

All orders must be prepaid in U.S. funds only. (Government entities may provide a purchase order—contact Safer Society Press for details.) Prices and fees subject to change without notice. All sales are final. Alaska, Hawaii and foreign orders, please see web site. Orders are accepted by:

• **Phone** 802-247-3132 weekdays from 8:30 AM to 5:00 PM ET. Requires payment with MasterCard or VISA.

• **Fax** to 802-247-4233 using this order form. Requires MasterCard or VISA.

• **Mail** order form with a check or money order, or with your VISA or MasterCard information to the above address.